2008 Contents

p59

p74

Poetry

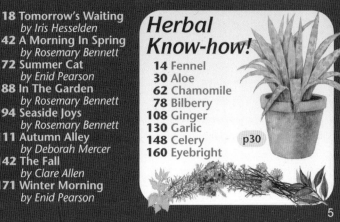
p42

Herbal Know-how!

p30

The Christmas

THE further through December it got, the more worried Zoe was becoming about the Christmas kiss.

It had all started as a joke with Ross. He was the caretaker at Hutton's community centre, where she worked as a yoga instructor, and she'd always liked him. She'd flirted with him a bit, too, if she was honest, but it had been pretty harmless flirting because they were just friends and there was no chance of them being anything else. For a start, they were both seeing other people.

Except that she wasn't any more, which she knew meant she should have stopped flirting. It was all very well when you knew nothing would ever come of it — but now things felt different, somehow.

She'd always been quite shy around men, but Ross had made her feel at ease from the moment she'd set eyes on him.

by Della Galton.

That had been on her first day at the centre, six months ago. She'd been as nervous as a kitten, and as she'd run up the stairs to the room where she was teaching, she'd dropped her kit bag. Her yoga mat had fallen out and slid down the stairs, almost tripping up the man who was coming up behind her.

"I'm so sorry," Zoe had said, bending to pick up the various bits and pieces that had fallen out of her bag.

"Don't mention it. Are you the new yoga teacher?"

"That's right, I'm Zoe. You're not a student, are you?"

Kiss

"No, I'm the caretaker. Ross," he'd added, grinning, and she had had a brief impression of brown eyes, dark brown hair, and warmth. "Would you like a hand with that lot?"

She'd accepted his offer gratefully, confessing to first-day nerves, and he'd offered to make her a calming cuppa before she started.

After that, they'd got into the habit of having a mug of tea together before her class.

IT wasn't really allowed. Yoga instructors — and every other type of instructor, come to that — were supposed to buy their tea out of the drinks machine. They were not supposed to have mugs brewed especially for them in the kitchen.

"I'll be getting a bill for this at the end of the year," she'd said a couple of weeks earlier, and Ross had grinned.

"I wasn't going to charge you — well, not in money, anyway. But I might have to claim a Christmas kiss," he said.

She'd laughed.

"Oh, might you?" And that had been that. She hadn't expected him to mention it again. After all, he'd been dating Melanie, who was a nurse, last time she'd asked, and she was going out with Terry, who was a long-distance lorry driver.

Or rather, she had been until last week, when he'd told her he'd met someone else.

She hadn't been nearly as hurt as she ought to have been. But then, deep down, she'd known it was coming. She and Terry had been drifting apart for weeks, and lately she'd had the feeling that some of his extended trips were just an excuse not to see her.

Zoe didn't know why she hadn't told Ross about this. Perhaps because she didn't want to unbalance things between them. It would alter the equilibrium

Illustration by Gary Long.

7

somehow, if he was going out with someone and she was single.

"Morning, Zoe. How are you today?"

She'd been so engrossed in her thoughts that she hadn't heard Ross come into the hall where she was setting up her CD player for the yoga class, and she jumped.

"You're not avoiding me, are you?" he asked.

"Avoiding you? Of course not." She glanced up into his laughing brown eyes. "Why on earth should I be?"

He began to count on his fingers.

"Seven days to go — I thought you might be trying to think of a reason for reneging on our deal."

"Well, I'm not," she said swiftly, regretting the words the minute she'd said them. He'd just given her the perfect opportunity to back out! Why hadn't she taken it?

"In that case, here's your tea." He grinned and put her mug on the window-sill beside them.

"Would you still have given me a cuppa if I had reneged on the deal?" she asked curiously.

"Of course I would. You know you've got me wrapped around your little finger." He grinned again and strolled out of the hall.

Zoe shook her head. She never knew how seriously to take him. Maybe he was just teasing her, and when it came to it, he'd let her off the hook altogether.

Suddenly, however, she wasn't so sure that she wanted to be let off the hook — and deep down, she knew that was why she hadn't said anything. The thought of kissing Ross was a prospect which was not at all unattractive.

HER last yoga class was three days before Christmas. Ross came into the classroom when she was packing things away and stood looking at her thoughtfully.

"What?" she said, glancing up at him.

"I haven't upset you, have I? You don't seem your normal, chirpy self."

"Of course you haven't. I'm just a bit tired."

"Well, you can have a break now, can't you?"

He came across the room and she was suddenly very aware of his presence and the fact that he was looking at her, his eyes unusually serious.

"Zoe, if you're worried about our deal, then please don't," he said. "I'm not going to insist you keep to your half of the bargain. I'll still make you tea."

"Perhaps I should get it out of the machine like I'm supposed to."

"There's no need. It was just a bit of a laugh. I didn't really expect you to leap into my arms. I know you and Terry are rock solid. I wouldn't want to muck that up." He gave her a wry half smile and she smiled back at him uncertainly.

Rock solid — if he only knew. She was about to tell him how wrong he was when he spoke again.

"Melanie and I have split up, by the way."

8

"Oh, Ross, what a shame. I am sorry."

"Don't be. It hasn't been working out for a while. It was mutual." He grinned ruefully and began to stack chairs, and she knew she couldn't tell him about Terry now, without seeming insensitive.

✳   ✳   ✳   ✳

"So how did it go?" Ross asked as he made her a cup of tea on the fifth of January, which was her first day back. "Did you enjoy yourselves?"

"Yes," she said.

"You don't sound very sure."

"OK, well, no, the truth is, things didn't go quite as planned." She sighed. "I've split up with Terry."

"Oh, Zoe, I'm sorry. What bad timing."

She felt heat in her face as she looked into his concerned brown eyes.

"Actually, we split up just before Christmas, but I didn't say anything," she said. "We'd been drifting apart for ages because he was always working. I think he preferred working to me."

"Must be mad," Ross muttered.

"What did you say?"

"Nothing." It was his turn to blush. Then he was backing out of the room.

When she went for her tea he seemed unusually edgy.

"Er — Zoe, I don't suppose you're free on Saturday, are you?" he said as she made to leave. "Only I'm going to a Christmas party and I wondered if you'd like to come with me."

"A Christmas party? In January?" She raised her eyebrows.

He grinned.

"Yes, it's with my walking club. They always have a late Christmas do because it's easier to book in January. Don't come if you'd rather not. I can go on my own but I just thought — maybe if you were at a loose end?"

"I'd love to come. Thanks."

THEY were dancing to a slow song, swaying to the music, their arms lightly around each other, and although she'd never been this close to him before, it felt totally right.

"Enjoying yourself?" Ross murmured.

"Yes, I am." She looked up into his eyes. "You?"

"Very much. Now, about this Christmas kiss . . ."

"But it's not Christmas."

"It looks pretty Christmassy to me," he said, indicating the eight-foot-high tree behind them, festooned with lights and decorations, and the gold and silver paper chains that draped the ballroom. And then he produced a sprig of mistletoe from his pocket and dangled it between them.

"Well, in that case . . ." She grinned at him and he bent his head and kissed her — the briefest, softest of touches of his lips to hers, as if he were just wanting her reaction.

Slightly breathless, she looked up at him.

"Can I consider my tea bill paid in full now?"

"Not just yet," he said, and kissed her again, and this time the room around them disappeared, the music faded into the background, and her legs felt a little bit shaky so that she was glad of his arms.

She closed her eyes, holding the moment . . . and when she opened them again he was gone! So were the ballroom and the music, and she was alone in bed clutching her pillow. And her brain registered, with crashing disappointment, that the whole thing had been a dream.

For a few, disorientated moments she wondered if Ross's invitation to the walking club's Christmas party had been part of the dream. But as reality crept slowly back, she realised that it hadn't. And that it was tonight.

✳　　✳　　✳　　✳

Ross picked her up at seven, as planned, and drove her to the venue. She didn't know whether she was relieved or disappointed to find that the function room was nothing like the ballroom in her dream. It was a lot smaller and in a converted bowling alley next to a pub. Stringy tinsel replaced the paper chains. The tree was artificial and there were bunches of fake mistletoe pinned up around the tiny dance floor.

The food was good, although it felt odd pulling crackers and letting off party poppers in January. It felt odd seeing Ross out of work, too, but not awkward. She felt as relaxed in his company as she always did, and by midway through the evening, she realised that she was having a really good time.

"Enjoying yourself?" he asked, and she had a brief flash of *déjà vu*, except that she wasn't in his arms, he was sitting opposite her at the table.

"Very much. You?"

"I'm having a great time. Fancy a dance?"

They'd been on the dance floor about five minutes when the music changed from lively to slow. He looked at her, his gaze quizzical, and it seemed as natural as breathing to move into his arms.

He held her lightly as they danced.

"I'm so glad you came, Zoe."

"Me, too," she said, thinking how uncannily like her dream this was.

But there was nothing dreamlike about his lips when he kissed her. They felt warm and very real on hers. And as she gave herself up to the kiss, the music faded away around them, and she was aware that her legs were a little shaky — just as they'd been last night.

With the part of her mind that could still think straight, she thought idly that nine times out of ten, reality didn't live up to your dreams. But now and again there was a glorious moment — like this one — when it was better. ▦

The Greatest Gift Of All

by Gerry McCullough.

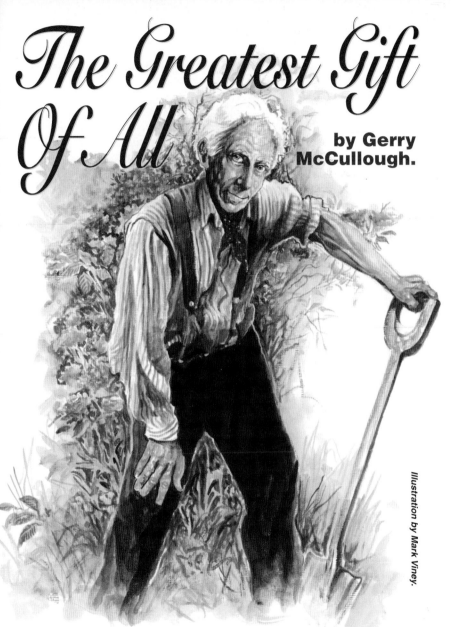

Illustration by Mark Viney.

THERE are some people who struggle for a large part of their lives trying to deal with a particular event in their past.

My grandfather was one of those. He was a good man, and he struggled hard to cope with his particular misfortune and get on with his life. Nevertheless, it had an effect — which for a long time he wasn't aware of — on the rest of his family.

11

My grandmother and my grandfather met when she was sixteen, and he a year or two older.

It was at a tent mission, which meant a gospel meeting in a large tent, in a field miles from anywhere. They had each gone along with friends of their own age.

It was one of the free entertainments on offer in those days before World War I. You could be sure of meeting a large crowd of young people, who would seldom be gathered together in one place otherwise.

The speaker was a gifted orator. At the close, when he called for people to come forward as a sign that they wanted to give their lives to the Lord, my grandmother Niamh Doherty stood up and walked to the front.

While she was waiting afterwards for her turn to pray with one of the counsellors, she noticed a young man standing next to her, also waiting. This was my grandfather, John Henry McCormick.

Coming out of the tent, he spoke to her.

"Beautiful evening, isn't it?"

Niamh agreed. It was a clear starry night.

"Come from round these parts?"

"Dromore," she said. This was a village some five or six miles away.

"A fair distance," John Henry said. "If you'd like some company for the walk home, I'd be glad to go along with you."

Niamh had plenty of friends who had come with her and would have kept her company on the way back. But, for all that, she accepted the offer.

What did they talk of on that first walk?

I don't know, and couldn't guess. My grandparents never talked to me about their personal feelings.

A S a child, I was closer to my grandfather than to anyone else, even my parents, although they loved me dearly, and I them.

Some of my most precious childhood memories are of standing by my grandfather's side as he worked at some job of carpentry around the house, and learning from him how to hit a nail firmly on the head, or how to wield a paintbrush.

"Stroke it gently, Johnny," he would say. "Don't go mad with it. Gently but firmly. Good boy! That's the way."

Often it would be he who would put me to bed, and tell me stories that set me laughing, or sing to me the hymns that he loved all his life.

Yet all I know about his deepest emotions, little enough as it is, I heard years later from my grandmother Niamh.

I remember her standing by the kitchen sink, washing dishes, as she told me the story of their early life, and I dried each dish as she handed it to me.

For the next year, after their first meeting, they saw each other regularly, and both their families seemed happy enough with the understanding that had come about between them.

Then John Henry went away to fight in the war.

For over four years, Niamh waited for him. He was a volunteer, you understand. Irishmen, even in the north of the country, were not conscripted in those days.

I T was the first real disagreement Niamh had had with him, and although it was made up before he sailed, she could see no reason for my grandfather to go, and indeed held a strong conviction that all war was wrong.

But John Henry held an equally strong belief that it was his duty to go and fight. And although Niamh was no moral weakling, and was not to be persuaded out of her conviction, my grandfather, a man of great strength of purpose, remained firm in his.

He survived the war unharmed, and in this he was unusual enough among the Irish who fought.

He came back to find himself with no job, and little prospect of one, and to a country which was to be torn with passion and violence for many years to come.

This time, he saw eye to eye with Niamh, and had no desire to be involved, on either side, in the bitterness which was pulling his country apart.

It was not easy to keep out. In their church, among his Army friends, in the linen factory where he eventually got a job, pressure was heavy on them to go with the crowd.

In the end, John Henry felt obliged to leave the Presbyterian church which he and Niamh had joined after the Mission. He threw in his lot with a small group who called themselves "brothers", later known generally as the Plymouth Brethren, who believed, like Niamh, that all fighting was wrong.

John Henry, with his war record, sat awkwardly among them in some ways. But that was the past, and for the present, he and they were in whole-hearted agreement.

With the job in the linen factory for security, my grandparents decided to marry. They had known each other for nearly seven years by now, and although it would not have been uncommon, in those days of poverty, for a couple to wait for much longer, no-one could accuse them of rushing into it.

Things were still difficult, with violence all around. After a few months, my grandparents decided to move to Scotland. John Henry had been offered a job in an engineering works. With their parents' help, they bought a small cottage in a little village within an easy cycle ride of the works, and settled down.

Before the first year of marriage was up, my grandmother was pregnant, and in due course she bore a fine, healthy, female child. The girl was christened Mary, and both my grandparents were delighted with her, although Niamh knew well that John Henry's heart had been set upon a son.

"Time enough for that," was all he said to her upon the subject, and when Mary was coming up for three, and Niamh was pregnant again, he made his pleasure obvious. Niamh hoped for his sake that she would have a boy this time, though, for herself, she was unconcerned.

When the second girl, my mother Betty, was born, John Henry said little. He still expressed his satisfaction in public, and indeed I believe he loved the child dearly, but to Niamh he said, "It's the Lord's will, Niamh, and when He means me to have a son, He'll give me one."

The next pregnancy was slower in coming. After a few years. Niamh had almost stopped looking for it, until in the end she was taken by surprise.

This time she prayed for a boy, and a boy it was — but not without a

Fennel

YOU may be surprised to learn that fennel was supposed to have supernatural powers in mediaeval times. Combined with St John's wort and other herbs, it was hung over doors on Midsummer's Eve to warn off witches and other evil spirits!

Fennel has long been known as a herb to aid digestion, and fennel seeds were even once regarded as a cure for body odour. The oil was thought to have a balancing effect on the female system and to increase the flow of body energy.

Fennel tea was mistakenly thought to have a slimming effect, but has been found to ease stomach pains and help expel gas, so perhaps it just relieved bloating — making it look as if the person had lost weight!

long, hard struggle. Niamh came back almost from the brink of the grave, and learned that there would be no more children for her.

It was a blow, but not a serious one, for hadn't they got Mary and Betty, and now wee Johnny, too?

He was a beautiful baby, plump and fair and always laughing. John Henry was full of joy every time he came into the house and saw him, and Niamh loved him as every mother loves her newest baby, in spite, or perhaps because, of the pains she had been through to have him.

As for Mary and Betty, their noses were not put out of joint, for they were delighted to have a new baby to play with, and were the envy of all their friends.

In the evenings, after his day's work, John Henry would sit with the baby on his knee, teaching him his first words, and younger in spirit himself than Niamh had seen him since he came back from the war.

"What are you teaching the youngster, Johnny?" she asked him on one occasion. "Sure, he can say 'Mama' and 'Dada' as right as rain already, and him only ten months!"

"Amen!" John Henry told her. "I'm teaching my boy to say 'Amen!', Rosie."

know-how!

Niamh went back into the kitchen laughing, and ten minutes later came running out in a panic at John Henry's roar. But she need not have worried. It was no calamity.

"He said it, Rosie! He said it!"

And sure enough, the baby was making a sound that was near enough to "Amen" to pass muster.

John Henry swung the child up into the air, and danced about the room with him.

"That's the way, fine boyo!" he exulted. "You'll never go far wrong, Johnny, if you can say, 'Amen! So be it!' to the Lord's will."

Niamh couldn't help laughing at the pair of them. Wee Johnny was laughing, too, as his father swung him about.

"Will you give over, for dear sakes, and sit down here to your supper while I put the child to bed!" she exhorted him, and presently peace was restored.

Johnny continued to grow and thrive. Niamh nursed him through a bad bout of chicken pox, and John Henry sat up at night with her until the worst was over.

Then there was the time when he fell, chasing the hens, and gashed his leg badly. But it healed up safely, and he was none the worse for it.

IT was just before Johnny's third birthday that scarlet fever broke out in the village.

Mary and Betty brought the news home from school. Lizzie Edwards and Tommy McKenzie were both off, and said to be very bad.

Teacher had said that school would have to be closed because of the risk of infection — "What's that, Mammy?" — and the nurse would be coming round to check up on all the children over the next few days.

Niamh, while naturally sorry for the Edwards and McKenzie families, and unable to keep entirely free from worry about her own three, wasn't unduly concerned.

Nurse, when she came to look at the girls, was cheerful and reassuring.

"No trouble there, any road," she said with a wide beam. "Two healthy weans as any I've seen the day. Now, just let me have a wee skelly at the child, before I go, and that'll be us all set up."

Johnny was coughing slightly, and didn't seem just his usual self. Nurse frowned when she heard him, and looked serious for a moment. Then she smiled again, and spoke heartily.

"Well, probably nothing much wrong there either. Still, put him to bed and keep him warm, Rosie, and give him a spoonful of the bottle I'm going to leave you. And I'll mention to the doctor to maybe call by and have a wee look at him."

Something cold settled on Niamh's heart.

Johnny was put to bed, and began to get worse. Less than a week later, he slipped quietly away out of life.

My grandmother told me, as she talked to me long afterwards, something of the struggle John Henry had had to deal with this bitter pain. He left the house, and for hours walked through the night.

Early the next morning, she found him sitting alone on the rocks by the edge of the shore. During that long night, he had somehow found words of comfort, coming to him out of the darkness, and at last he had accepted them.

When Niamh found him, he looked round at her and smiled, and she saw that he was whole and at peace again. He said nothing to her of his battle with grief.

The only words he spoke were, "Let's go home, Rosie. I could do with a cup of tea."

OVER the following years, Niamh saw with content the bond between John Henry and their two daughters grew deeper and stronger.

He never spoke of wee Johnny. Niamh knew that there was pain still there, beneath the surface, but it seemed to her that he had found healing in watching his two daughters as they grew up.

When Mary won a scholarship to the grammar school, he was happier than she had seen him for a long time, and when both girls expressed a desire to become part of the church, she knew that, like herself, he felt a deep, wordless satisfaction.

The two girls grew strong and healthy. Niamh was pleased, also, to see that they were both growing prettier all the time, though she could never get her husband to acknowledge any pleasure in this.

"It's the heart that matters, Rosie," was all he would say.

Niamh quite agreed, but, woman-like, she felt that Mary's tall slender figure and sweet smile, and Betty's merry, mischievous face, so blooming and attractive, were an added bonus for which she was very thankful.

One evening, when John Henry was sitting by the fire, and Mary and Betty struggled with their homework, Niamh saw that Betty was stealing frequent glances at her father's sad, abstracted face. She could not claim to be surprised when, next afternoon, Betty seized the chance of being alone with her mother, to ask questions.

"Why does Daddy always look so sad, Mammy?" she asked. "Is anything wrong? Is it anything I've done? Or Mary?"

"No, no, darling!" Niamh responded quickly. "It's nothing to do with you!"

Then, seeing from Betty's face that more was going to be needed, she blurted out hurriedly, "You remember your wee brother, Johnny?"

Betty nodded.

"Well, Daddy still feels very sad to have lost him. He always wanted a son. When Johnny died, he felt very bad about it."

"He always wanted a son?" Betty repeated slowly.

Niamh looked at her daughter's face, and realised that she had said the wrong thing.

"Of course, he loves his two wee daughters as well," she tried, attempting to heal the effect of her hasty words. But she saw, even as she tried, that it was too late.

MUM! Mary!"

Betty bounced into the cottage one evening with her face glowing.

She flung her arms round her mother, hugged her sister, then thrust out her left hand for them both to see.

A diamond, even if quite a small one, sparkled on her third finger.

"Betty! Oh, darling!" was all Niamh could say at first. Then she began to ask questions. "It's Doctor Murphy?"

"Mum!" Betty protested. "Of course it is! How many boyfriends do you think I'm going out with?"

They all laughed, more for happiness than because it was particularly funny.

"And you must start calling him Tommy, Mum. You know he's asked you to lots of times." She looked round. "Where's Dad?"

"Upstairs in his room, reading."

"Well, don't say anything to him yet, Mum. Tommy thinks he should ask Dad for my hand. Very old-fashioned, isn't he? But I like it."

"Your daddy will like that, too, Betty," Niamh said. "Bring him to tea tomorrow, why don't you, and they can settle it then."

Dr Tommy Murphy had been appearing for tea fairly often recently. He was a quiet, big man, not in his first flush of youth, but then, neither was Betty by now.

Betty's family all liked him, but Niamh, for one, had had little suspicion of any romance. To tell the truth, she had stopped expecting either daughter to marry some years ago.

She found it hard not to comment on the situation to Mary, when they were preparing scones and sandwiches for tea the following day.

"It's lovely to see your sister so happy, Mary. Would you not think of following her example now?"

Mary, a tall, sweet-faced girl with a strong will of her own, merely laughed.

"Mum, you've been trying to marry me off since I was eighteen! But I love teaching, and I love the kiddies, and it would take a lot to make me give it up."

"Betty loves her job, too. She's certainly a born nurse. But see how she's met the right man through it? Maybe that might happen to you?"

But Mary only laughed again, and said, "We'll see!"

Betty, as she made it clear, didn't intend to give up nursing entirely, on her marriage.

"Since the war, Mum, lots of girls have got used to working and being in responsible positions. I love my job. I know I'm doing something worthwhile. When the family comes along, I expect I'll stop for a while, but then I'll want to go back part-time. Maybe you and Dad would help out with baby-sitting if Tommy's on duty? Especially if it's a boy," she added with a slight bitterness in her voice which distressed Niamh.

Rannoch Moor.

Tomorrow's Waiting

*T HE new year lies before us
With days unlived and new,
Tomorrow's waiting, out of sight,
The road's still out of view.
Like morning-fresh, untrodden snow,
Unmarked by human feet,
A hidden path to lead us on
Where old and new friends meet.*

"Yes, of course we will, love," was all she could think of to say.

BETTY'S wedding day seemed to come round in a flash.
Suddenly Niamh and Mary, so lovely in her pale lilac bridesmaid's dress that Niamh's heart turned over as she looked at her, were leaving for the church.

Betty, ready to the last rosebud, sat side by side with her father on the shabby sofa in the small front room of the cottage, and wondered what to say.

She and her father had talked so little over the last few years. When the two girls came home on leave from the war, they had found plenty to say, sharing

And shall we fill the coming year
With thoughts to make or mar?
Or will we reach a brave, new world
And reach out to a star?
So, as we tread the days ahead,
May goodwill flow in streams,
And may our lives be worthy yet
Of all our hopes and dreams.
              — Iris Hesselden.

with their father their military experiences. But, since then, the wells of communication seemed to have dried up. Different, I suppose, if I had been a boy, Betty thought.

John Henry looked like a stranger to her, handsome and even distinguished in his formal wedding clothes. She leaned over and adjusted the single white rose in his buttonhole.

"There, Dad! Now you look the part!"

"Thanks, love," my grandfather said.

He caught hold of her hand before she had time to withdraw it.

"Betty, I don't know what to say. You're going away to a life of your own. But you know I'll always love you. You'll always be my little girl."

Betty, looking up at him, saw with amazement that there were tears in his eyes.

SUDDENLY her own tears, bottled up for years from the hurt she had known since her teens, gushed out.

"Oh, Daddy!" she sobbed. "I'm so sorry I wasn't a boy!"

"What?"

"I know it was what you really wanted," Betty sobbed. "I wish I could have changed things for you. But how could I? But maybe now I can make it up to you by having a grandson?"

John Henry looked at her for a silent moment. Then he swallowed hard.

"Listen, Betty. I'll be honest with you. I did want a boy at one time. I suppose every man would like to have a son. And losing wee Johnny was the hardest thing that ever happened in my life. It took me a while to get over that, I know. But I've long since dealt with it.

"A grandchild would be great. But I honestly don't care if it's a boy or a girl. I just pray it'll be healthy, if the Lord chooses to bless us with one or more. And let me tell you something." He swung Betty round to face him, put a hand under her chin to raise her face, and looked her straight in the eyes. "This is the truth I'm telling you. I wouldn't change either of my lovely wee girls for all the sons in the world."

Betty looked at him, and knew that it was true.

John Henry put his arms round her, and together they sobbed away the hurt of years, and found comfort in each other's love.

Then John Henry came back to the present with a start.

"Dear save us, girl, we're due at the church in ten minutes! And look at you!"

Betty's pretty face was streaked with a mixture of tears and mascara.

"You've been wearing that make-up I always forbade! Well, see what comes of it! Away with you into the bathroom, and see what you can do about your face!"

Betty gave a gasp of horror, and rushed for the bathroom. Then she put her head back round the door, and smiled mischievously at her father.

"Dad! I'm not the only one who needs repairs! Hadn't you better brush that powder off your fancy jacket?"

WITHIN six months, Betty was expecting.

Niamh was very happy, and as for John Henry, he was bursting with delight. He found himself wondering if it would be a boy.

Then it came to him with renewed force that what he had said to Betty was completely true. Boy or girl, it didn't matter. He knew how happy this new child would make him.

It wasn't an easy birth. Betty was older than the normal young mother of those days. Niamh and John Henry waited anxiously in the visitors' room at the hospital. Tommy, as a doctor, had chosen to be with his wife during the birth. Surely it was taking too long?

Could it be that there were problems?

My grandparents held each other's hands, and prayed silently.

John Henry saw, as never before, how great a blessing any child born safely, boy or girl, would be to them all.

Then, at last, the door opened, and Tommy came in, carrying a little bundle. They could see at once from his beaming face that all was well.

Niamh had never seen my grandfather so happy as when he looked down and smiled at the new baby. He looked as if a miracle had happened.

Then, she told me, something happened which was, in its way, an even greater gift, coming unlooked for and unsought.

"Congratulate us!" my father Tommy said, coming forward, and proudly, he showed my grandparents their new grandson. "Isn't it wonderful! There's another wee Johnny in the family!" ■

Provand's Lordship, Glasgow

*M*Y Glaswegian parents moved to Aberdeen before I was born, but I spent most of my school holidays there, staying with an aunt and uncle. Every Sunday, one of my uncles would take me on a tram ride to various interesting places with a poke of sweeties. I thoroughly enjoyed these trips.

The "dear green place" remains special to me still.

— *Mrs E.M., Aberdeen.*

J. CAMPBELL KERR.

O K, here we are." Mel took a deep breath as she stopped the car. She pulled on the handbrake and looked over at the school playground with all the children in dark blue uniforms running round, making the most of being outside before lessons started.

"All right?" Mel turned to look at Harvey.

"Fine," he said, clutching his new school bag and looking anything but fine.

"Let's go." Mel was trying to be jolly, but she felt nervous. She so wanted him to be happy.

"I made you welsh cakes for your lunch," she said, a little too cheerfully.

"Great!" Harvey grinned. Then suddenly his face dropped. "But what if no-one wants to sit with me?" he asked.

Mel suddenly felt a sharp pain somewhere deep in her heart.

"Darling, you're

Illustration by Gerard Fay.

going to find loads of new friends. It'll be OK, I promise." Mel hoped with all her heart that she was right and it would be OK.

It had been hard enough when he'd started school a year ago. But then Tony had been made redundant and hadn't been able to find another job locally, so they'd had to move to a new town. Tony had joined a new printing firm — and now Harvey was about to start school all over again.

They walked hand-in-hand towards the playground, but as they approached the low wall, Harvey pulled his hand away. Mel tried to suppress her feeling of hurt.

When he was younger, he'd always turned to her for security, but she knew

Helping Harvey

by Jo Thomas.

*Illustration
by G. Long.*

it wouldn't look cool, holding her hand. Maybe this was what they meant by cutting the apron strings.

But she was worried for him. What if he didn't make any new friends?

She could remember what that was like, being a Forces' child. They'd moved from country to country, school to school, and she'd never wanted that for her child. They had to make it work here. She didn't want to move again.

They both stood for a moment, looking at the throng of noisy children.

Some were running about, weaving in and out of the crowds, while others were in huddles looking at bracelets and keyrings all made from the same sort of plaited plastic strings . . .

"What's your name?" A young boy was standing at the wall, looking menacingly at Harvey.

Mel instinctively put her arm round him — and he didn't shrug it away this time.

"Harvey," he replied sullenly, trying to match the boy's tone.

"Harvey's new," Mel put in. "What's your name?"

"Joseph." He stared at Harvey, sussing him out. "How many

Scoobies you got?" he asked.

Harvey glanced up at Mel, then just shrugged and looked at the floor.

"Um . . . Joseph . . . what are Scoobies?" Mel decided it would be OK for an un-cool mum to ask, but not for Harvey.

Joseph laughed in the derisory way that only little boys can.

"Scoobies — you know, these!" He held up a keyring bursting with short and long, fluorescent and sparkly plaited plastic strings.

"Oh, they're the 'in' thing, are they?" Mel asked. Joseph looked at her blankly.

"In my day, it was Rubik's Cubes," she jollied. Joseph still looked blank.

The bell rang just then and with a collective groan, all the blue uniforms fell reluctantly into lines in front of the door.

Harvey swallowed and looked up at Mel.

A couple of teachers came out and the young blonde woman Mel recognised as Mrs Saunders waved to her and Harvey. She waved back and gave Harvey a gentle nudge. She wanted to hug and kiss him and tell him she loved him, but felt that with Joseph still sizing him up, it was better just to smile and wave as they filed in.

Harvey headed off and stood reluctantly next to Joseph, leaving a respectable distance. He didn't look back as they filed in and Mel felt that little pain in her heart again.

Back in the privacy of her car, she was finally able to let out the huge sob that she'd been swallowing back all morning, and then she cried and cried as if her heart would break. She felt a whole lot better once the tears began to dry up.

At least now she knew how to help Harvey, she thought as she put the key in the ignition. The engine chugged into life and she set off on her mission.

*   *   *   *

"Excuse me, have you got any Scoobies?" Mel asked the girl with a selection of earrings in the corner shop.

"Over there." The girl looked up from her magazine and waved at a stand of packets of plastic strings.

Mel picked up a packet and brought them back to the till.

"You're lucky — we've just had a delivery," the assistant remarked. "They'll be gone by the time the kids get out of school."

"Popular, are they?" Mel asked.

"Oh, yes, they're all at it," the girl replied.

Mel picked up the local paper, too, paid and hurried out. She'd have to learn how to plait the Scoobies before Harvey got home so she could show him. Thankfully, full instructions were enclosed.

As she threw her purchases on to the passenger seat, an advert on the front of the newspaper caught her eye.

Kitchen assistants wanted. St Peter's Primary School. Experience preferred.

Mel smiled, delighted. That was it! St Peter's was Harvey's school. With all her catering experience, she'd be well qualified for the job, and with Harvey now in school she'd been thinking she should start looking for employment. It would certainly help financially, and she'd be able to keep an eye on Harvey at the same time.

She rang the number as soon as she got in, to request an application form.

"We'll put that in the post for you today," she was promised, and she hung up, feeling a twinge of excitement. It was all working out perfectly.

Working at the school, she'd be able to keep a close eye on Harvey. She just had to hope she landed the job.

Now all she had to do was master the art of Scoobies.

She ripped open the packet and stared at the four diagram instructions. She tied four of the strings with a knot at one end.

"Then take the first string and loop it over the second." Mel found it helped to talk through the process out loud. When she wasn't giving herself instructions, she poked her tongue out of the side of her mouth and frowned, concentrating for all she was worth.

"Take the second and loop it over the next two. Or was that three? Which was the first? Oh, bother!"

And she started all over again.

"Take the first string. Which one did I start with?" If she'd started with four different colours it would probably have been easier.

By twelve-thirty she still hadn't managed to make her Scoobie look anything like the picture. She shoved it into her handbag and headed back to the school. She wanted to give Harvey the Scoobies during his lunch break. It might cheer him up a bit.

"MUM!" Harvey was in the playground when she reached the gates and he spotted her almost immediately. Mel's stomach flipped over — was there a problem? But then she noticed he was smiling.

"Hello, love."

He let her bend over the wall and give him a quick hug. As she did, she noticed that the same lad was loitering nearby.

"Oh, Joseph, isn't it?" Mel asked warily. Joseph nodded.

Mel lowered her voice to speak to Harvey.

"I got you these." She pulled the packet of Scoobies out of her bag.

"Scoobies, great!" Harvey held them in both hands.

"I haven't worked out how to do it yet," Mel whispered. "But don't worry, I'll have it sussed by the time you get home."

"Oh, don't worry, I can do it."

Harvey pulled out four strings, tied them together and started flipping loops here, there and everywhere until the series of knots looked just like the diagram.

"Wow!" Mel was stunned.

"Look, like this, Mum." Harvey passed the strings to Mel and held her hands as he guided them over and through each other.

"Wow!" she said again. "I've spent all morning trying to do that. How did you know how to do it?"

"Joseph showed me — look!" Harvey pulled out a keyring with a couple of Scoobies on it. Joseph grinned.

"How did you manage that?" Mel whispered to Harvey.

"I swapped some welsh cakes for a Scoobie lesson." He grinned and turned to his new friend. "Come on, Joseph, let's see if we can finish these off." He held up Mel's Scoobies.

"What are you doing here anyway, Mum? It's not home time."

"Oh, I . . . I just wanted to check, you know, check . . . everything's OK."

Harvey looked at her askance, his earlier worries forgotten.

"Of course everything's OK." He grinned. "See you."

He and Joseph ran off together, laughing.

MEL smiled through her tears and returned home, where she immediately picked up the phone and called up the council office once more.

"Yes, we have an application form ready to send out to you," the secretary said, in answer to her query. "It should be with you in a couple of days, if that's all right."

"Actually," Mel said apologetically, "I don't think it's the right job for me after all. I'm sorry. Could you take my name off the list, please?"

Mel felt a lump in her throat as she hung up. Her son needed his own space — and perhaps she should be thinking of something that was just for her. Maybe it was time to start thinking of herself as well as Harvey.

She grabbed a tissue and blew her nose.

"There might be another job in the paper that'll suit me."

She'd managed to calm herself down by the time she went to pick Harvey up later.

"Mum, can you make me some more welsh cakes for tomorrow?" he asked eagerly. "I've got loads of friends who want one."

"Of course I can." Mel smiled as she looked down at his grinning face. Her baby might be growing up, but he still needed her. He just didn't need her there all the time.

She was still smiling later as she laid out the ingredients for the welsh cakes for all Harvey's new friends.

They weren't cutting the apron strings — they were just stretching them a little. ■

Sound Advice

I KNOW it's not traditional to get on well with your mother-in-law, but then Lady Annabel Duncan is not your average mother-in-law. She's not your average Lady, either, although perhaps I should say that I don't really have much to compare her with, having never met anyone else with a title.

I'd had visions of her living in a draughty old Scottish castle with chandeliers and aged, loyal staff. The reality was a Dundee semi in a pleasant tree-lined avenue with central heating and four bedrooms.

by Katie Lewis.

Illustration by Mike Heslop.

"My mother's as nutty as a fruitcake," Iain had told me cheerfully the first time we'd discussed our parents. "She used to breed dogs until we got over-run with them and Dad moved out."

"How do you mean 'over-run'?"

"She had about forty at one time — although we had a smallholding then and most of them were outside."

"How many has she got now?"

"Six or seven, I think."

"Well, that's not so bad, is it?"

"You haven't seen the size of her lounge," Iain muttered darkly. "She's got bats as well, but they're mostly in the shed."

"Mostly," I echoed.

He grinned.

"Bats are very misunderstood creatures, you know. But — hey — Mum will tell you that herself."

IN fact, Iain's mum had been so warm and so eloquent on the subject of both bats and West Highland terriers that I'd been smitten. With her, that is — not her menagerie.

From what Iain had said, I'd been expecting his mother to be a cross between Penelope Keith in "The Good Life" and a bag lady, but she was neither.

She was rather beautiful — tall and chic with high cheekbones and warm brown eyes and auburn hair which curled elegantly around her slender neck and shoulders.

Iain went to make us ginger tea, which was her favourite drink, while she interviewed me for the position of future daughter-in-law. Her words, not mine. She was the kind of person who could get away with saying things like this without either causing offence, or leaving you in any doubt that she was serious.

"So, Vanessa — tell me about your parents," she murmured, smiling at me over her bone china mug. "Do you still speak to them?"

"I get on well with Dad," I said, a little startled at her directness. "But I lost Mum three years ago. She had a heart attack when she was fifty-two."

"How tragic. Were you very close?"

"We argued — like most mothers and daughters," I said truthfully. "But, yes, we were close. I miss her very much."

"I always wanted a daughter to argue with," Annabel remarked wistfully. "It's not the same arguing with your sons — or your husband, come to that."

I smiled and she narrowed her eyes.

"But all that is yet to come for you, Vanessa. Tell me about your career."

So I told her all about my job in Accident and Emergency, which was where I'd met Iain when he'd come in with a broken leg after a skiing accident, and she listened in fascination. Then she told me the rather convoluted tale of how she'd inherited her title, her brains and her looks, but sadly not a penny to go with them, from her late mother.

Iain told me later what she'd proclaimed me to be.

"Warm, with just a wee hint of spice, rather like her tea, and very satisfactory."

LOOKING back, I sometimes wonder if we'd have got married if she hadn't liked me. Iain said it wouldn't have made any difference — but I'm not so sure. Gloriously eccentric she might be, but she has a head like ice when it comes to getting her own way.

During the eight or so years of our acquaintance, I've never known Annabel not to get exactly what she wanted. She always has the last word on everything.

That's why I'm here today, despite the fact that Iain and I separated a couple of months ago.

At first I'd said no when she'd phoned to see if I was coming over for Mother's Day, as per our usual arrangement.

"Now, Vanessa, you must come. I don't care what's happened between you and Iain. It's the one day of the year that I have no intention of spending alone."

"But surely Iain will be with you," I'd protested.

"No, he won't, because he's gone skiing in Banff. He probably hasn't even given a single thought to the date."

So, against my better judgement, I went. And now we were sitting in Annabel's lounge in the company of three of her favourite Westies.

"So, how are you feeling?" Annabel asked, studying me in a way that told me she knew far more about our split than she ought to have done.

"Absolutely fine."

"Don't lie to me, Vanessa. Have some more tea — ginger is very good for morning sickness."

"How on earth did you know?" I gasped. "Iain doesn't even know. I don't want him to know, either — I couldn't bear him coming back just because I'm pregnant."

"An educated guess," Annabel said smugly. "And don't be so stubborn, Vanessa. What better reason could there be?"

"Because he's sorry would be a good start," I snapped, marching across to the window and staring out at the row of yellow daffodils nodding sagely in the border. "And because he loves me would be good, too." I spun round, close to tears, but my mother-in-law's face was unusually gentle.

"You know he loves you. He worships the ground you walk on. He always has."

"Well, he's got a funny way of showing it." I wished she hadn't mentioned morning sickness. For the last couple of weeks, just the thought of it had been enough to set me off. And it was happening again.

My stomach lurched alarmingly, so I was forced to put my hand over my mouth and make a run for the bathroom.

SHE was sitting where I'd left her when I got back, rather to my surprise. I wouldn't have put it past her to have locked all the doors so I couldn't escape.

"It's not my business, Vanessa, but have you considered the fact that you might be — well, a wee bit responsible for Iain walking out?"

"You're right, it's not your business," I snapped, "and no, of course it isn't my fault."

"You didn't tell him to go, then?"

I stared at her in amazement. There was no way she could have known that. Iain wouldn't have told her. He didn't make a habit of talking about relationships, in much the same way

Herbal

Aloe

NOWADAYS aloe is best known to us as aloe vera — a mainstay ingredient of several skincare products. Did you know, however, that aloe was used by the Greeks as early as the fourth century for medicinal purposes? The leaf juices have antibacterial, antifungal and antiviral compounds that help prevent wounds becoming infected and speed up the repair of burns, bites and other skin maladies.

The aloe may look like a cactus, but it is actually a member of the lily family. It's very handy to have around the house as a plant — you can use aloe if you suffer from a burn. Simply cut off the outer leaf of an aloe plant, split it open and squeeze the leaf gel on the burn. Not only will the aloe gel immediately soothe the pain of the burn, but it will speed up your skin's recovery time.

he didn't make a habit of arguing. Well, not my kind of arguing, anyway, which always involved a lot of shouting.

"I thought so," Annabel said with a satisfied tone. "Sit down, Vanessa. And stop being so angry. It's not good for the baby."

I sat — even though I'd rather have thumped her. But I didn't fancy my chances against all those Westies. They might have looked small, but I'd seen the way they hurled themselves at the front door when the hapless postman pushed anything through the letter-box.

"I know Iain would never have left you unless you'd asked him to go," she continued quietly. She stroked the dog on her lap as she spoke, reminding me, rather irrationally, of the way the baddie in James Bond films always strokes a white cat when he's about to deliver an order to kill someone.

"Just as Iain's father would never have left me if I hadn't forced him out."

"I thought he went because he couldn't handle living with forty dogs," I blurted out, before I could stop myself.

"Och, no — we could have coped with that." Annabel waved a careless hand. "He went because I made him go. It was as simple as that. I was impatient and stroppy and stubborn and Keith was — well, he was a dear,

Know-how!

sweet man." Her eyes misted over.

"He wasn't a very good communicator, though. Especially during rows. He'd clam up, and point blank refuse to argue with me.

"I threw him out to get a reaction — and I got one all right, but not quite the one I'd hoped for." Her face shadowed. "And Iain's very like his father. So what was it he did that made you tell him to go?"

I couldn't meet her eyes.

"He had an affair with a girl at work."

"Are you sure? If you'll forgive me saying so, it doesn't sound like Iain at all."

"I caught him kissing her at a works do."

"A kiss isn't an affair, though, Vanessa. Did he admit that he was having an affair?"

"Not exactly, no," I snapped, glaring at her and wondering how on earth we'd got to this point. "He said I was over-reacting. The cheek! I wasn't the one sneaking about in corners with someone else."

"And so you threw him out. Well, I can quite see why. Would you like some more ginger tea?"

"No, thanks. I think I'd better go. Annabel, I know you're only trying to help, but I've said far too much already. And, please, Annabel, I'd appreciate it if you didn't tell Iain about the baby. I don't want him coming back to me out of duty."

I COULD never do that," a voice said from the doorway, and I spun round in shock.

"You said he was in Banff!" I accused.

"I lied," Annabel said softly. "I don't approve of lying, Vanessa, as you know. But sometimes the end justifies the means. As in this case, I think you will find."

And with that she rose gracefully, strolled past her son and shut the door on us. I heard the key turning in the lock.

"You put her up to this," I yelled.

"Of course I didn't. You know as well as I do that no-one puts Mum up to anything. She's a law unto herself."

"She can't lock us in." I glared at the door.

"I think she already has.

"Please, Vanessa, hear me out. I don't like this any more than you do."

He didn't come any closer, which was just as well. He leaned back against the door, his face strained.

"I didn't have an affair."

"A fling at a party is just as hurtful."

"Oh, come on, Vanessa. It wasn't a fling, as you know perfectly well. It was just a kiss. And *she* kissed me. *I* was trying to extricate myself."

"Well, it didn't look like that to me. And if that's the case, why didn't you tell me before?"

"I did try. But you weren't exactly in the mood to listen." His eyes, the same colour as his mother's, darkened a couple of shades.

"You were so furious. You had a right to be furious, I know, but it was out of proportion to what happened."

I glared at him.

"I'm still furious."

"I can see that," he said ruefully. "And I'm sorry. When did you find out about the baby?"

"Just after you went."

HE nodded. He still didn't move, but his quiet rationality was beginning to get through to me. I knew he was right. I had over-reacted a bit.

Well — OK — a lot. I'd caused a massive scene at his work.

And the next day we'd had another row about that, during which I'd thrown his entire Joni Mitchell CD collection out of the bedroom window because they'd been playing a Joni Mitchell song when I'd witnessed *that* kiss.

I was a bit like Annabel, I reflected, a touch guiltily. Impatient, stroppy and stubborn summed me up perfectly. With a cocktail of pregnancy hormones thrown in, I was probably lethal.

"It was a pretty passionate kiss," I said grudgingly. I wasn't about to let him off the hook completely.

Iain looked at me steadily.

"Not on my part," he said. "But I'm sorry, Vanessa — truly I am. It was unforgivable. I should have seen it coming and avoided it. I promise it won't happen again."

"It had better not."

He took two cautious steps towards me.

"Can I come home?"

"All right."

He hesitated in the middle of the room and I went slowly across and put my arms around him, because I supposed it was definitely time that I met him halfway on this.

Then the door opened — and the timing was so perfect that it struck me that Annabel must have been listening on the other side of it.

"I took the liberty of booking a table for three at the Crooked Beams for lunch," she said brightly. "Mother's Day special." She beamed at us.

"Shall I get my coat?"

"Do you always get your own way?" I asked her, half exasperated, half amused, as Iain went up to order our Sunday roasts.

She smiled.

"More or less, if it's important." Then her face sobered.

"Vanessa, you know I'm not one for giving advice, but if I could just say one wee thing."

I nodded, knowing she would anyway.

"Having the last word might feel very satisfying at the time, but it's not all it's cracked up to be. Sometimes it's the worst thing you can do."

"Are you talking about Iain's dad?" I asked softly.

"I am. Yes." She blinked a couple of times. "You see, my dear, four weeks after I threw him out, he died suddenly. And I've always regretted that the last words we ever had were cross words. It fairly made me realise how petty our quarrels had been. But it was too late by then."

I swallowed. What terrible words, *too late*.

I'd known Iain's father had died after they'd separated, but Iain had never mentioned the timing.

"And you didn't want me to make the same mistake with Iain."

"Something like that. I just wanted you to see it in perspective. I never could." For a moment I could have sworn I saw the glint of tears in her eyes. But perhaps it was a trick of the light.

Iain had told me plenty of times that his mother only ever cried when she lost one of her dogs.

"Thanks," I murmured. And on impulse I leaned across and kissed her.

*   *   *   *

"We're very alike, you and I," Annabel pronounced later, when we'd finished our meal.

"You mean we're both argumentative and impatient and fiery," I challenged her, a twinkle in my eye.

She smiled.

"No," she said, folding her serviette neatly and putting it on her plate. "I mean we're both passionate and warm-hearted and generous to a fault. Which reminds me, I'm getting this bill." She signalled to a waiter.

I caught Iain's eye and we grinned at each other.

And the future suddenly seemed a whole lot brighter. ▪

G O on, Bill, I dare you," I challenged as we watched the waltzer slow to a halt. A crowd of noisy teenagers stumbled off the brightly-coloured fairground ride which only seconds before had been spinning furiously.

It was a bit rotten of me to dare him, but if a big sister can't occasionally be mean to a little brother then something's far wrong!

Every summer for as long as I could remember, we'd taken a trip to the fair. Even if we didn't indulge in too many of the rides these days, we tried to get into the spirit of things with our hot-dogs, toffee apples and candyfloss.

We always came away from the fairground with the latest pop tunes ringing in our ears and a sense of childish excitement in our hearts.

"You dare me, eh, Ellen? That's fighting talk. I haven't been on one of these rides for years." He thought for a moment.

"I'll do it." He chuckled. "But only if you do it, too."

"You're on," I said, to his surprise.

We clambered on board the waltzer, Bill with his dodgy leg and his walking-stick and me with my umbrella. We were quickly joined by a couple of young lads, and the attendant locked the safety bar into position.

He gave us a funny look. I guess he hadn't seen too many over-sixties on his ride before! The two young lads looked a bit surprised to see us there, too.

"I'll have to keep these in the booth during the ride — for safety," he told us, picking up the walking-stick and umbrella.

A few moments later the raucous music

"I Dare

Illustration by David Young.

34

started and the ride began to rotate, steadily gathering speed until the lights became a blur. I clung on to the safety bar, my knuckles turning white.

My heart thumped as the adrenaline pumped through my veins and I couldn't stop the laughter which bubbled in my throat.

As the ride spun wildly I let out a scream. I hadn't felt so invigorated in years! I was being bumped painfully in the spinning car, my hair was probably standing on end and my glasses had slipped down my nose, but I felt like I was fifteen again.

A few minutes later the ride slowed to a standstill and I snatched a glance at Bill. Under his greying hair, his face was glowing with excitement, his grin as wide as a Cheshire cat's. The two lads jumped off nimbly, heading back to the queue for another go, but we climbed carefully off the ride, both of us more than a little shaken up.

"That was great! I haven't felt that exhilarated in years," Bill gasped, full of bravado. Then he gripped my arm as if he was about to collapse.

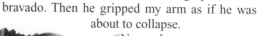

"Now where can we get a cup of tea? I need to sit down and recover."

Chuckling at our bravery — or stupidity — we staggered, arm in arm, to a large tent offering tea in plastic cups.

"There's nothing like a bit of a thrill to wear you out," Bill said as he flopped into a plastic chair which wobbled alarmingly on the uneven ground.

"Careful, Bill." I put out a steadying hand. "You've already got a dodgy knee. You don't need a broken arm to go with it! You'd be no good to your customers with your arm in a sling."

*　　*　　*　　*

When Bill had retired from the fire service a few years ago he'd started up his own gardening

by Julie Dickins.

35

firm. He pruned and mowed, weeded and dug and was never happier than when he was knee deep in mud.

"Speaking of my customers, Ellen, there's something I want to talk to you about."

He hunched his shoulders and his laughter lines were suddenly replaced by a pensive frown.

"I'm in a real dilemma and I don't know what to do for the best."

I looked at him, surprised. This wasn't like my brother at all.

"Spit it out, baby brother. A problem shared is a problem halved."

As we sipped our tea he told me why he looked so worried.

"I just can't decide what to do," he finished. "It's such a big step and I'm not sure if I'm brave enough to take it."

He sighed as if the weight of the world was on his shoulders. But I had never been more sure of anything.

"Go on, Bill, you've got to do it. I dare you!"

HE stopped, putting down the plastic cup on the table so quickly that the tea splashed out on to the paper tablecloth.

"You dare me?" he repeated, looking irritable. "This is a serious decision, Ellen, not some childish prank."

"Yes, I know, but what have you got to lose?"

He looked at me crossly.

"I could lose a really special friendship, Ellen," he said seriously. "And you know how difficult it is to find someone on the same wavelength at our age. It's no time for jokes."

"But just think what you could gain," I insisted. "I know it's a big decision, but just think of the rewards."

He took another sip of tea, playing for time. It was a ploy he'd used a hundred times before; pretending to be busy while he weighed up the pros and cons of the dare.

When he was eight, I, his big sister who should have known better, dared him to race his home-made go-kart with the wobbly pram wheels down the biggest hill we could find.

He did it, too, but only after a minute spent fruitlessly searching for something in his bulging pockets. Delaying tactics!

"I'm not a chicken," he'd yelled before careering down the hill straight into the lake at the bottom. A young man in a suit on a lunchtime walk had helped him out of the water as I had looked on with tears of laughter rolling down my cheeks.

Luckily he wasn't hurt, but the state of his clothes when he got home made my mother go mad at him and I had had a hard time keeping a straight face as she scrubbed at him with a rough flannel, muttering all the time about boys and their crazy stunts.

That was over fifty years ago, but the memory was so vivid it could have been yesterday.

"What are you grinning at?" he asked, a moment later.

"Remember your go-kart?" I said.

He paused to think for a moment.

"The one with the wobbly pram wheels that ended up in the lake?" His grey eyes twinkled. "Boy, was I scared bumping down that hill, and all you did was laugh."

"I helped you pull the go-kart out, didn't I?"

"And didn't Mum give us what-for when we got home." He chuckled. "My new jumper was ruined."

I dredged up the comic recollection of a soggy beige jumper hanging around Bill's knees.

"It was the one Gran had knitted for your birthday."

He rubbed behind his ear thoughtfully.

"I'm lucky Mum didn't permanently remove a layer of skin the way she was scrubbing at me."

"She was worried you caught something from the dirty water in the lake. It was when she insisted on giving you castor oil that night to clean you from the inside that I laughed the most, though!"

There was a moment of silence between us as visions of our escapade swam before us.

BILL and I had nicknamed ourselves the "daredevil duo" when we were little. We issued the usual childish dares to climb trees, balance on walls and swing across the stream on the rope the older boys had set up many summers before.

Even the most mundane of activities was subject to a dare. I dared him to eat all his cabbage; he dared me to go to sleep without my teddy. Our childhood had been filled with laughter as we bravely took on all that life could throw at us and conquered all our fears.

Now here we were, fifty years on, still facing life's challenges together as if we were children.

"What about the time," Bill recalled, "when I dared you to clamber into old Webley's garden?"

My mouth watered at the memory.

"He had raspberries and loganberries by the pound on those bushes and all I managed to get was a measly handful before he marched out, waving his stick and yelling at me."

"You were back over that wall like a shot."

"Yes, and you could have warned me that Constable Dykes was heading our way. He gave me a real telling-off for stealing and told me if I ever did it again I'd go straight to jail."

We both laughed.

"We were reckless, weren't we?" Bill said at last. "Always up to mischief of one sort or another."

"Yes, but it was fun and we didn't hurt anyone except ourselves occasionally. Being brave made us feel more alive than playing it safe like we were supposed to."

"You're right, sis." He squeezed my arm affectionately. "Riding that waltzer reminded me how it felt to have the old adrenaline pumping again."

"Go on then, Bill," I said softly. "What's stopping you? Be reckless just once more. You know it's the right decision."

"You're right." He smiled. "Playing it safe is dull. Nothing ventured is nothing gained, after all. I'll do it, Ellen. I'll go straight round when we get back. Wish me luck!"

THE next afternoon, as I pruned a particularly vicious rose, Meg, my neighbour, called over the fence.

"Ellen, do you fancy a cuppa? I'd really appreciate your advice."

"I'll be right over — just give me a minute to freshen up."

I pulled off my gardening gloves, glad of the break.

"You've worked wonders with your garden, Meg," I said a few minutes later as I wandered over her newly-mown lawn. Spring flowers nodded merrily in the borders lining the path to the front door.

"It's not all down to me." She smiled. "I don't know what I'd have done during the last year without your Bill giving me a hand. He really is a treasure."

I smiled back.

"I'm glad I suggested that he help you."

"Actually, Ellen, Bill is the reason I need your advice," Meg said shyly, busying herself with the tea things.

"I'm sure you know that we've been spending a lot of time together lately and we get on so well . . ." Her voice trailed off as if she wasn't quite sure how to carry on.

Honestly, what was wrong with my brother and Meg? They were meant for each other and I had realised it from the first moment I met my new neighbour.

"Meg, you and Bill make a really lovely couple," I reassured her. "I don't remember the last time my little brother looked so happy."

It was true. He'd had a definite spring in his step as we left the fairground yesterday.

"Oh, I'm so glad you said that, Ellen, because he's asked me to marry him!" She blushed furiously. "I really wanted you to approve."

"That's great news, Meg!" I grasped her hand, trying to sound surprised. "Have you said yes, yet? Go on, I dare you!" ■

Going Courting

by Sheila Culshaw.

Illustration by Len Thurston.

IT was three o'clock in the morning. Mr Joshua Horrocks woke up suddenly. Why? Because he could hear the strange sound of knocking at the bedroom window. Was there a burglar about?

Then Joshua realised it was only the sound of the window-pane rattling. The sash window was always left slightly open to let in fresh air and a breeze was blowing.

Next, four dozen clocks suddenly started to chime downstairs; not all at once, either, but making a fragmented and confusing din which put paid to Joshua's chances of getting back to sleep.

He lay on his side and worried. He lay on his back and worried. As the sky lightened and dawn came creeping through the small gap in the heavy velvet curtains he was still worrying.

Joshua was worrying about Agnes Atkinson again.

His parents were dead and he had no brothers or sisters and no immediate family to advise him. What's more, he was a bachelor of forty-six years.

Joshua Horrocks was lonely and he was in love.

Yes, he had a thriving jewellery business and a comfortable home, but Joshua wanted a wife. To be precise, he wanted Agnes Atkinson to be his wife.

He thought about his appearance as he lay there worrying, and decided he was reasonably attractive, although his hair was turning grey. His prospects were good, his business successful. Should he pluck up the courage to speak to her, and if he did, would she accept his offer? This was his quandary.

He kept turning the problem over and over in his mind, until his head started to ache. Would Agnes Atkinson say "Yes" or "No"?

"And I won't know until I ask her, will I?" he finally said out loud to the bedroom, silent except for the ticking of the clock.

Joshua knew he would feel terrible if Agnes turned him down; that it would mean an end to their close friendship and their musical evenings together.

He decided he might as well get up. So he put on his thick grey woollen dressing-gown and slippers and marched down the stairs to start the working day.

OUTSIDE the immaculately painted shop gleamed a heavy gilt sign. It read *Joshua Horrocks — High Class Jeweller*, in large copperplate lettering. He had hoped at one time to add *and Son*, but this had never happened because he had never found the right woman — until now.

Joshua was a rather shy and retiring gentleman. He relied on his assistant, Cyril, to do most of the selling whilst he concentrated on repair work and running the business. And Joshua was particularly shy with the ladies.

Agnes Atkinson was one of the leading sopranos in the choir at the Bethel Chapel in Marchington Road. She sang sublimely three times every Sunday. Her "Ave Maria" and "Abide With Me" brought tears of emotion to Joshua's eyes every time he heard her voice.

Unfortunately, though, there was a great deal of arguing amongst the female singers in the choir as to who would sit on the front row of the choir stalls and Agnes had managed to squeeze on soon after she joined. This was because the choirmaster had heard her exquisite voice.

The innovation had caused considerable jealousy amongst the other ladies who held on to their entrenched positions on the front row because of their length of time in office.

But Agnes, placid and calm, managed to squeeze in and ignored any bickering. She knew she could out-sing any of the others, and eventually everyone calmed down and started to like her.

Joshua watched her carefully from his own position amongst the tenors and tried to sit near to her at every choir practice on a Tuesday night. She was an attractive woman with big grey eyes, luxuriant hair and a solid, well-corseted figure.

He had a fine tenor voice and played his parents' upright piano, which was in the parlour of his house, beautifully. So when Agnes told him over tea in the vestry that she wished she had an accompanist to help her improve her musical talents he immediately volunteered to provide his skills.

Of course, there was gossip. People whispered behind backs that there was something "going on between them pair". It was well known that Joshua Horrocks was "worth a bob or two" and it looked like he would soon be sharing it.

The altos whispered to the basses that a certain woman who was in the front row of the choir was having singing lessons in a certain tenor's house. Although Agnes had told them about it quite openly, still significant looks were passed.

Some of the ladies were jealous but most were pleased, because Agnes was a warm-hearted person, always ready to do a good turn, and everyone respected Joshua Horrocks.

SOON it was reported that the sounds of "Love's Old Sweet Song" and "Who Is Sylvia?" were floating out into the street and that Joshua Horrocks was a changed man — bright eyed, chatty, even.

When customers came into his shop, that young Cyril could hardly get a word in edgeways. The whole town knew well before Joshua Horrocks did that he was "courting" Agnes Atkinson, spinster of the parish.

Joshua was a decent, upright and considerate man and felt that he must offer Agnes his hand in marriage as soon as he started to hear all the rumours.

But that morning when Joshua had not been able to sleep, it was because he was afraid.

He knew that he would have to somehow pluck up the courage and ask her to be his wife, and he was going to do it that very day.

Joshua wondered how to approach this most serious of matters. They were meeting in the town park at two o'clock because it was Wednesday, half-day closing in the town. Now, what could he take to impress her, he wondered?

He went into the double back yard that he had converted into a small garden with raised flower-beds, now full of bright annuals, then into his small greenhouse. There was his answer. He would take some of his specimen chrysanthemums to offer her.

Six of the most perfect were chosen in shades of rich bronze, yellow and amber. He loved the bitter scent, but would Agnes? Some people hated chrysanthemums.

But surely Agnes wouldn't fail to appreciate these huge, tightly curled blooms that had been grown so carefully and with such meticulous care?

They were each prize-winning examples he had cultivated for the annual flower show. What better gesture could he give than this to the woman he loved? To give up his possibility of winning first prize? Their round faces beamed up at him as he carried them inside to put them into a bucket of water.

He was busy all morning repairing watches in the shop, whilst Cyril served the customers, but underneath the surface Joshua was nervous.

What would happen if she said "No"? What if he felt and behaved like a complete fool in front of her? Joshua knew he was staking his entire future on the answer to one question this afternoon.

If she refused him she would never again come to their little soirees during the week. And how could he possibly face her in the chapel each Sunday, or escort her into the vestry and talk to her over a cup of tea?

A Morning In Spring

*D*EEP in the greenwood, the songbirds are waking,
Softly and sweetly they're starting to sing,
Soon the air fills with their jubilant chorus,
Greeting the dawn of a morning in spring.

On the high banks of a lane in the country,
Petals unfold as their beauty they bring,
Primrose and celandine gleam in the sunshine,
Delighting our gaze on a morning in spring.

THERE were a few people walking in the sunshine in the town park when he arrived on the dot of two. Some were watching the wide variety of ducks with their children by their sides, laughing and smiling and feeding the squawking birds with bread.

The trees were in full leaf. The scent of the evenly spaced rose bushes was faint and delicate, wafting through the air.

42

Down in the orchard, the trees are in blossom,
An exquisite spectacle fit for a king,
Pink and white petals adorning the branches,
Their loveliness gracing a morning in spring.

Swallows are swooping, the cuckoo is calling,
Butterflies flutter each delicate wing,
Hedgerows are budding, their leaves are unfurling,
These things delight on a morning in spring.
— **Rosemary Bennett.**

But when Joshua saw Agnes walking towards him his knees started to quiver. She looked so confident, moving towards him straight across the grass with a smile on her sweet, open face.

Today she was wearing a simple cream dress, a cream, wide-brimmed straw hat and short, openwork cream gloves. Joshua noticed her arms were soft, plump and rounded, the skin pale and delicate as lilies.

As she drew nearer he knew he wouldn't know what to say. He knew he would make a mess of this whole procedure. He was too much of a coward to do the thing properly.

He noticed that quite a few people sitting on benches under the trees were covertly glancing over in their direction, so he pulled himself together.

"Hello, Agnes, how are you, my dear?" he said shyly.

"Fine, Joshua, and you?"

"Oh, very well. Couldn't be better." Joshua pulled out an immaculate handkerchief and wiped his fevered brow.

"What a beautiful display of chrysanthemums you have there. Why, they are absolutely perfect. Why on earth have you cut them? You could have shown these. My father always loved chrysanthemums," she said sadly.

"Did he? Well, these are for you, Agnes. I hoped you would like them. Not everybody does."

"Joshua, they are quite my favourite flowers. Thank you so much." She took the golden bouquet into her arms. "They are Mother's favourite flowers, too. She always used to put four in a huge pottery vase in the front window when I was young. I can remember them now, how the parlour smelled of their scent. But no chrysanthemums that Father ever grew were half as

43

enormous as these."

Impulsively, Agnes caught hold of Joshua's hand. Joshua could feel his face going red with embarrassment.

"They'll last you for ages, Agnes. Four weeks at least, if you change the water regularly. Even longer if you put an aspirin in the water when you change it," he said nervously.

"I'll try that. That's a good tip," Agnes told him.

Joshua offered Agnes his arm. She was exactly his height, but if she had no heels on her boots she'd be considerably smaller than him, he thought tenderly. Yes, they were a perfectly matched couple.

"Well, what shall we do first, take a turn around the lake, or sit on a bench in the shade?"

"Sit in the shade, I'm afraid, Joshua. My complexion doesn't take kindly to sunlight. That is one of the disadvantages of having auburn hair. My skin burns so easily."

Joshua thought her thick auburn hair was her crowning glory, even if it was slightly flecked with grey at the sides. In his opinion Agnes Atkinson was a beautiful woman.

Luckily, there was an empty bench under an oak tree in full leaf that provided ample shade. Joshua wiped his handkerchief carefully over the seat before Agnes took her place.

"So I'm coming back to tea, am I? Mother has gone to visit her friend, so there will be no need for me to rush back home," Agnes told him placidly.

"Yes, you are. Cyril and I have prepared quite a little feast. I thought that later we might try out 'With Verdure Clad'?"

"I'd like that," she told him with a smile.

HE looked deeply into her eyes, his own thoughtful and worried. How on earth was he going to ask her his important question? He simply couldn't do it.

But gradually his heartbeat subsided when he looked into those kind, grey eyes. He reminded himself that this was Agnes, Agnes with the beautiful soprano voice, Agnes the woman he wanted to be with for the rest of his life.

He would care for her mother as if she were his own, too. They could all be a family.

Joshua by nature was a careful man, but now he threw caution to the winds.

"Agnes, I have a very important question to ask of you."

"Yes?" Agnes smiled softly, expectantly.

He just couldn't do it.

"Can you play a musical instrument? I've never asked you that before."

"No, Joshua, I cannot. I learned to play the recorder when I was young, but that's about all. It's singing that I enjoy, the wonderful feeling when the entire choir is around me and all the voices are merging and soaring together in harmony. There is nothing better."

"I can understand that . . . Agnes?"

"Yes, Joshua?"

"I believe I know what is your favourite jewel. Shall I guess?"

Agnes's eyes sparkled with fun.

"Please do."

"I think that you would favour diamonds, Agnes. Am I right? I have knowledge about these matters, being in the trade for twenty-five years." He laughed.

Agnes smiled.

"No, Joshua, you are wrong. I think I prefer rubies, although diamonds are beautiful in their own way. But the depth of colour in a ruby is incomparable."

"Oh," Joshua said, his voice now quite desperate. He had thought this was the ideal way of introducing what he really wanted to say. His experience of twenty-five years in the jewellery trade had obviously failed him. He could have wept.

"Whatever is the matter with you, Joshua? You look as though you've 'eaten your beddin' ', as Father used to say when he saw me looking fed up and miserable." She laughed.

"It was just that I was sure that I would know which jewel you would prefer for your engagement ring, Agnes, and I've brought you this as a small offering. But you can have a ruby ring if you prefer, just as long as you will become engaged to be married," Joshua said, all in a rush.

Then he produced the most perfect little band of diamonds in warm Welsh gold.

"Of course I will marry you! Why, I'd marry you tomorrow, you silly man. Surely you must realise that by now! And this ring is the most perfect I have seen in my life and I have suddenly decided I don't like rubies one little bit."

THE observers sitting around them all smiled. They'd known exactly what was going to happen. But they all looked discreetly away as the couple rose to their feet to walk back through the park for their boiled ham tea.

"I think we'll have a sip of elderberry wine to celebrate with, shall we, Agnes?" Joshua said daringly, beaming all over his face. "I have two bottles hidden away in a cupboard."

"Why, I think we could manage maybe two or three sips," his new fiancée teased.

She put her arm through Joshua's and it was observed by passers-by that she no longer wore her ladylike open weave gloves.

No, they were stuffed inside Agnes's reticule, so she could display her diamond ring to the world at last. ◼

To Fly Like An Eagle

"T HESE," Alex said earnestly, waving the binoculars, "are definitely the best present ever! I'm bound to see an eagle with these, aren't I, Mum?"

"If we do spot an eagle, you'll certainly get a good view," Carol agreed.

"Fingers crossed," her father-in-law, Greg, murmured as he carefully pushed Alex's wheelchair down the narrow path to the river.

Although he hadn't meant Alex to hear, his ten-year-old grandson replied confidently.

"I know we'll see an eagle, Grandpa! The guidebook says there are loads of golden eagles in the Galloway Forest Park. Well, at least six pairs anyway. Surely we'll see one flying overhead!"

"We're a fair way from the forest park here," Carol reminded him.

Alex was undaunted.

"Yes, but eagles have a wide range, don't they?"

Carol shrugged and smiled as she helped Greg manoeuvre the wheelchair down to the landing stage. Her son's eternal optimism was a constant source of amazement to her.

"Can I ring the bell for the ferryman?" Alex cried.

"Molly's already rung it," his dad, Steve, answered. He was standing on the jetty holding tight to toddler Molly's hand.

Nevertheless, Alex pulled the jangling bell-rope again and watched with satisfaction as the little boat came chugging over the river to meet them. Steve lifted Alex into the boat while Carol folded up the wheelchair.

"Next stop, Threave Castle," the ferryman announced cheerfully. "But seeing as you're my only customers, I'll give you a wee ride up the river first."

Alex dangled his fingers in the water as the boat purred away. The boatman pointed out the birdlife and told them about the otters that could be seen along the river.

"And they do say there's an osprey," he added. "But you have to get up early in the morning to see him."

"Any golden eagles?" Alex asked eagerly.

The man shook his head.

"Not round here, I'm afraid. Maybe farther over west in the hills."

"We'll go there later this week," Steve said, tickling Alex's neck.

"Soon," Alex insisted.

*   *   *   *

They crossed the river to the picturesque little castle standing in ruined dignity over grassy slopes.

As she chatted to the guide, Carol watched Alex whizzing around in the wheelchair, chasing Molly. His little sister shrieked happily and ran to Grandpa for shelter.

"I'm Archibald the Grim!" Alex yelled. "Coming to get you in my war chariot!"

"Oh, dear, they're making a terrible racket!" Carol fretted. She began to

by Catherine Laybourn.

Illustrations by David Young.

47

move towards the children to quiet them, but the guide reassured her.

"Don't worry — there's nobody else here to be disturbed. You picked a nice quiet week for your holiday."

Carol nodded, thinking of the special arrangements she had made to take the children out of school. Luckily the headmistress had understood that they needed this holiday, the first with Alex in a wheelchair, to be a quiet one. Alex didn't need crowds of other children staring at him . . .

"They're enjoying themselves, aren't they?" the guide commented.

"Yes, they are." Then Carol went on quietly, in answer to his unspoken question. "He's . . . It was a traffic accident last year."

She still relived it in nightmares. The incredulous moment when she realised the van at the lights wasn't going to stop; the sickening crunch as it ploughed into the side of the car . . . and then the heart-stopping fear for her son, trapped in the back . . .

SOMETIMES the dream was so terribly vivid that she woke with her heart pounding. Then she had to get up and tiptoe into Alex's room, convinced he must have woken, too — but he was always sleeping soundly. Carol would creep back to her own bed and weep into her pillow until Steve reached out to comfort her.

She couldn't have coped without Steve. So solid and practical, he just tackled each problem as it arose. He came over now and put an arm around her shoulders, while the guide tutted sympathetically.

"Is there anything they can do?"

"There's a lot they can do," Steve said confidently. "They think he'll walk again, eventually; it'll just take time."

Carol bit her lip. That wasn't quite what the doctors had said. Steve was sparing the guide's feelings — and her own . . .

Tiring of the game, Molly threw herself down on the grass to pick daises with Grandpa. Alex took out his new binoculars again and scanned the sky.

"Look!" he cried. "Look, up there! It's an eagle, I'm sure it's an eagle!"

"It might be an osprey," Steve suggested.

"Sorry — but it looks like a buzzard to me!" the guide, more knowledgeable, said. Then, as Alex's face fell, he continued. "I'll tell you what: you should go and see the red kites at Loch Ken. They have a feeding station there, so you're sure to get a sight of them if you go at the right time."

"We'll do that," Carol said gratefully.

She would have gone to the ends of the earth if it could make Alex's holiday a happy one. She didn't know why he'd developed this sudden interest in birds of prey — but if an eagle was what he wanted, that was what she must somehow provide . . .

Next day, in search of eagles, they drove over to Glen Trool in the heart of the forest park. But to Carol's dismay the skies were low and overcast.

"Do you think we've really got any chance?" she murmured to Steve.

He shook his head doubtfully.

"Not much . . . Never mind, it's still beautiful here."

"Try telling Alex that!"

"I will." With a flourish, Steve produced the digital camera.

He spent the next hour encouraging Alex to take pictures, discussing composition and wheeling him around in the hunt for perfect photos.

After a while Carol offered to take over.

"Molly's quite happy trying to fill up the loch with pebbles," she told him. "Why don't you and your dad go off for your walk? You know you're longing to go and trek up a hill together!"

But Steve shook his head.

"No, I don't mind. Not on this holiday."

"I'm fine here," Greg agreed. "Hey, Alex, who do you think can take the daftest picture — you or me?"

"Me!" Alex cried.

So they all had to take turns posing and pulling faces in the competition to take the Daftest Picture In The World.

"We'll put them on the laptop computer to see them properly when we get back to the cottage," Steve promised as he loaded the wheelchair back into the car.

"I think Molly's picture of her feet will win." Alex grinned and Carol ruffled his hair. It had been a good day. They'd forgotten all about the quest for eagles . . .

But then Alex turned the camera back to the hills, holding it ready to snap while he gazed into the sombre sky, and Carol realised that he hadn't forgotten at all.

After a few moments he lowered it with a sigh, and gave her a small, twisted smile.

"Maybe we'll see one tomorrow," he said.

NEXT day it rained. Even Alex agreed gloomily that no eagle in its right senses would be out in this weather, and no bird-watcher either. Instead, they spent the morning playing board games and doing jigsaws in the vain hope that the weather would clear.

It didn't, so the family drove off to Wigtown and spent an afternoon contentedly trawling the shelves of the second-hand bookshops.

Soon Greg was loaded down with volumes on fishing and music, and Molly had discovered a treasure chest full of nearly-new colouring books.

Meanwhile Carol was delighted to discover a pile of the old comic books that had amused her in her childhood.

"Just look at these!" she told Alex. "I remember this very one from thirty years ago. I couldn't believe it when Granny chucked it out. Would you like me to buy it for you?"

Alex flicked through the book and laughed. But then he put it aside.

"No, thanks, Mum. Can I buy this one instead, please? I know it's a bit expensive but I could use my holiday money."

Carol looked at the big, glossy book on his lap. "The Golden Eagle And Its Habitat." Although she couldn't have spelt out why, her heart sank.

"Are you sure?"

"Yes, please. Please say yes."

"Well, if that's the one you really want," she agreed with a shrug, and wheeled him over to the counter.

With Alex engrossed in his new purchase, she touched Steve's sleeve.

"I don't know if we ought to be encouraging him in this eagle thing," she murmured. "It's becoming an obsession with him. What if we don't see one? He's going to be so disappointed!"

"I know. We'll try the forest park again tomorrow," Steve promised. "We'd have a better chance farther north, though. I wish he'd told us about this passion for eagles before we booked the holiday!"

"We were looking for a wheelchair-friendly place," Carol reminded him. "And Alex never mentioned eagles until a few weeks ago. I just don't understand where it's all coming from."

"Don't you? Eagles fly high," Steve said softly. "They're masters of the air. To Alex they mean freedom. That's what I think, anyway."

"Freedom? But . . ." Carol fell silent, pondering, understanding.

"Steve, how can we find him an eagle?"

"We can't. But we can always go and see the red kites again on the way back to Dalbeattie. In the meantime, I think I'd better buy you that comic book you've been clutching so tightly . . ."

"THE red kites are great," Alex said wistfully. "It's just that I really did want to see an eagle."

"Maybe on our next holiday we can go up to the Outer Hebrides," Carol suggested. "But you never know — we might see one today."

Privately she doubted it. A chilly wind ruffled the surface of Clatteringshaw's loch, and the sky behind the hills was as dull and grey as lead. Only a few other people huddled on the benches near the visitor centre.

And tomorrow they were going home . . .

"The only trouble is," Alex said, "that might be a bit tricky. I mean, getting

Braemar Gathering

WHEN I think of the Braemar Gathering, I recall a coach holiday a friend and I took there.

The driver took us down to Crathie on the Sunday morning to attend the church service. What a wonderful morning it turned out to be! The Queen Mother and Prince Charles were also there, and after the service they left by the side door where Her Majesty was joined by a number of local children. She seemed so happy.

What a great privilege to have been in the right place at the right time!

— *Mrs G.W., Lancs.*

J. CAMPBELL KERR.

around — you know, with the wheelchair. It might be better to wait until I'm walking again." His voice dropped. "But that could be a while."

Carol put an arm around him. Her heart was wrung, but she managed to keep her voice steady.

"I know. But we'll keep working on it, won't we?" She glanced around for something to distract him.

"Look, the café's open. How about an ice-cream?"

Steve groaned.

"In this weather?"

"It's perfect ice-cream weather!" Alex protested. "They don't melt! Strawberry, please, Mum!"

"Chocolate for me," Molly piped up.

Carol was relieved to be able to turn her back on her family and walk to the café.

Luckily there was nobody to see her chin wobbling; no-one to notice the tears suddenly filling her eyes, apart from a family on the next bench who were so busy arguing that they were oblivious to everything else.

She had to stand in the doorway for a moment to compose herself. When Alex was walking again . . .

Alex might walk again, with sticks, if he was lucky. But he would never run. Never kick a football, never turn cartwheels round the garden. Never again have the freedom that they all took for granted . . .

She took a few deep breaths and went into the café, and by the time she returned to her family she was smiling again.

*　　*　　*　　*

Alex held his ice-cream in one hand and his binoculars in the other, gazing steadily upwards through them as he absent-mindedly licked the cone.

"When you've finished freezing your stomachs, maybe we could go and try this out?" Greg opened his rucksack and produced a model boat.

"Radio controlled," he said. "I bought it yesterday in Wigtown. I thought it might be fun."

"That's great," Alex said, but without enthusiasm.

Wearily he lowered his binoculars at last and held out his ice-cream.

"Mum, do you want some of this? I'm not as hungry as I thought."

"You all right, sweetheart?"

"Yes, but can I have a hug?"

Handing the cornet to Steve, Carol knelt down and Alex buried his face in her shoulder. She could see Greg distracting Molly with the boat.

She felt the chill breeze on her neck, and heard the raised voices of the other family behind her.

"No, you can't have an ice-cream! You just had a cola!"

"But, Mu-um . . ."

"And quit whining. I'm sick of hearing you."

"I'm sick of hearing the pair of you," the father's voice said. "I'm trying to read my paper here, and all I can hear is you two going on."

"But, Da-ad . . ."

"I wish we'd left you in school! Shut up and eat your crisps!"

Alex raised his head and took a long breath.

"Can we try that boat out now, Grandpa?" he said.

"Sure thing," Greg agreed.

As Carol bent to release the wheelchair's brake, Alex put his mouth close to her ear.

"Mum? It's been a great holiday. Really. It's been brilliant. I don't mind if we don't see an eagle. It's not that important really, is it?"

"It's not the end of the world." Carol smiled down at him. "There are so many other things we can do."

✳　　✳　　✳　　✳

Steve pushed the chair down to the loch's edge, where Greg placed the boat in the water. It buzzed over the grey wavelets with a noise like a frantic bumblebee, veering and zig-zagging, until Carol saw Alex's pretended enthusiasm become real. When it was finally time to leave, he didn't even look up at the sky . . .

Automatically she glanced up herself. And there, wheeling across the silken clouds, was a shape that made her catch her breath; a pair of long, strong wings as straight as a glider's . . .

"Alex?" she murmured. "Where are your binoculars?"

"What is it, Mum?" He followed her gaze. "Oh, it's an eagle! Mum — Dad — look, look, it's an eagle!"

"It might be another buzzard," Steve warned.

But Greg shook his head in wonder.

"I don't know . . . that's big for a buzzard!"

"It's my eagle," Alex whispered. "It's our eagle, for ever and ever."

His free hand reached over and gripped Carol's. Together they watched the bird's slow, graceful spiral, climbing ever higher, until it dissolved into the great, wide, glorious sky. ▪

An Eye For

JEFF was like a cat that had got the cream as he emptied his bag of goodies all over the kitchen table.

"Plenty of bargains, love," he gloated as he rattled off his purchases. Twenty pence off a bag of flour; a pound off a medium chicken; ten pence off a hundred grams of boiled ham; twenty pence off a bag of potatoes and two packets of chocolate biscuits for the price of one.

I sighed and tutted. He'd done it again. I could just picture his face lighting up as he saw the special offers sign in the supermarket.

"But I didn't ask for a chicken," I said, pulling a face. "Or flour, or potatoes, and you know we decided to cut out the biscuits."

by R.A. Blackmoor.

Illustration by Mark Viney.

A Bargain

"Well, I couldn't find the list, love, and you know what I'm like at remembering. And I thought a few extra biscuits wouldn't hurt seeing as you enjoy them so much," he added, with that wicked grin on his face and twinkle in his eye.

"It's no good looking at me like that, Jeff Hammond," I scolded. "If this extra spending doesn't stop, there'll be no summer holiday for us this year."

Jeff, I remembered, had always liked to think of himself as frugal and now, with time to shop around, he positively loved a bargain.

It really started when he retired. As a concession to my arthritis, he offered to do the shopping.

"Save you trudging up to town every day, love," he'd said.

But as time went on he'd been drawn further into "saving a pound or two" as he called it. I was beginning to think I was not second-hand Neve, but half price Neve.

Even the flowers he brought from the supermarket on a Saturday always bore the label *Reduced*. We were bulging at the seams as well as freezer, pantry and cupboards with unwanted goods.

I'd voiced my opinion many times and it worked for a while, but then he'd be back again into the habit. I could cope with the odd item of clothing. It was the food budget that kept going through the roof.

MARGE, from next door, interrupted my train of thought as she coo-eed and came in the back door for her elevenses. With Jeff seated down in the sitting-room with his coffee, paper and a plate of chocolate biscuits, we sat down at the kitchen table to have a chat.

"I do wish my Stan was more like your Jeff," Marge complained. "He never budges out of the chair and when I see your Jeff coming back from the shops on a Saturday morning with flowers I wonder where I've gone wrong."

I smiled sympathetically. Yes, it was nice to have flowers — even if they were half-dead. But she didn't know what else I had to put up with.

"Do you know, Neve, I'm seventy next week and in the last thirty years I've never had so much as a bunch of flowers from him. He always thought it was a waste of money," she added. I felt a pang of sadness.

After Marge had wandered back next door, I sat at the kitchen table, totting up the shopping bill. Ruth, our daughter, and four-year-old Jessica came in through the back door.

"Hello, Mum," she said. "I can see Dad's been at it again with his special offers."

Pulling a face, I then turned to give my granddaughter a hug, but her eyes spotted the chocolate biscuits on the table.

"Granny, can I have one, please?"

"Yes, lovey," I said, giving her a cuddle. "Help me eat them up!"

*　　*　　*　　*

The following Saturday morning, when Jeff came into the sitting-room with his hat and coat on, he found me ready and waiting to go shopping.

"Are you coming to check on the spending, love?" He smiled, shaking his head in amusement.

"Well, someone has to." I grinned back at him.

I pulled the shopping list out of my pocket on entering the supermarket and Jeff immediately drew my attention to the first basket inside the door.

"Look, love, jam, buy one get one free, and it's the best. How about we have a slice of crusty bread with some blackcurrant jam for tea?"

For a moment, I thought I could smell the bread cooling on the rack in my mother's kitchen.

My good intentions went flying out of the window as a few seconds later two jars went into the trolley — one blackcurrant, one strawberry.

We moved a little further on, then Jeff spotted trifle mixes — buy one, get one free.

"It's been ages since we had a trifle, love, and you could make Jessica one for her tea on Sunday."

I relented. Seeing as it was for my granddaughter, two trifle mixes went in the trolley and two tins of strawberries, which were also on special offer.

By the time we got to the checkout, the shopping list had been abandoned and I'd become one of the special offer brigade — not quite as bad as Jeff, but I could see how easy it was to be lured.

NOT only were my knees giving me gyp, but my mood was a little frayed, to say the least, and my purse much lighter when we arrived home. All my good intentions had fallen by the wayside.

Jeff, wisely, didn't say a word. He just put the kettle on, made the tea, and then sauntered off into the living-room with the morning paper.

Still feeling ruffled, I opened the cupboard door to pack the tins away when three boxes fell out and caught me on the head. Jeff came hurrying in to see what the commotion was all about.

"We just can't go on like this, Jeff," I said firmly. "All these special offers have to stop. We've nowhere to put them and the place is bulging and so are we."

But almost before I'd finished speaking, an idea came to mind. Maybe it had been the knock on the head that did it! I shared my thoughts with Jeff.

"It sounds like a grand idea, love. I can do the invites on the computer and Jessica and I can decorate the room, while you and Ruth do the baking. And Neve," he added apologetically, "I'll try not to spend quite so much money in future."

A LL day Friday and most of Saturday, I sat at the kitchen table rolling pastry, filling cake tins, making trifles and flans, while Ruth busied herself lifting things in and out of the oven.

Jeff and Jessica decorated the front room with banners, streamers and balloons. We were like a hive of busy bees producing the most decorative and scrumptious delicacies.

At seven-thirty on Saturday evening all our neighbours and friends arrived dressed for the event.

The call for silence went through the air just before seven forty-five. Jeff opened the front door to Marge and Stan, making believe we were getting ready to go out to dinner with them.

Then he discreetly ushered them into the front room to wait. I quickly put the light on and the birthday chorus rang out as streamers and party poppers flew through the air. Marge stared around the room, unable to take it in.

There was Mike and Lilly from next door, Val and John from over the road, Mildred and Sam from number twenty-six, Connie and Bill from twenty-eight, her two sisters and their husbands, Stan's brother and his wife as well as Ruth, Jessica and Paul.

"You've done this just for me?" Marge said shakily. "I've never had a party like this in all my life."

Then, when Marge spotted the cake on the table that I'd made using my large oval meat dish, the tears trickled down her face.

There were just seven candles on it, one for each decade, and two tiny dolls' cups and saucers representing our elevenses. She threw her arms around me and I knew then all our efforts had been worth it.

Throughout the evening we laughed, told jokes, sang, played games, ate and really enjoyed each other's company. By the end of the night, Stan was even talking to Jeff about throwing a party himself and inviting all the neighbours.

Sinking into the chair after they'd all gone, Jeff put his arms around me.

"We couldn't have done it without the special offers, love."

I knew he was right. It'd been great to celebrate Marge's seventieth birthday and we'd used most of the excess in the cupboards and freezer.

"But this bulk buying just has to stop," I said, and he nodded his head in agreement and helped me up out of the chair.

✳   ✳   ✳   ✳

On Monday morning I felt a bit lethargic after a busy weekend and as I went out to put rubbish in the bin, Stan called over the fence.

"Is Jeff in, Neve?"

"Yes, he's just getting ready to go down to the shops," I answered.

"Do you think he'll spare me a minute?" Stan asked.

Ten minutes later both men were walking up the road discussing barbecues.

"I've never been one for parties, Jeff, but it was such a good night and my Marge enjoyed herself so much that I'd thought I'd try and please her by buying a barbecue. And seeing as you're a man who likes a bargain, I thought you'd know just the right shop."

An hour later the bread, milk and eggs I'd asked for had been forgotten as two tottering men came up the road carrying a large box each.

"I couldn't let this bargain go, love." Jeff was having a job getting in the back door. "It was reduced to twenty-nine pounds!"

"What do we want a barbecue for?" I retorted angrily. Jeff had gone just too far this time.

With another thirty pounds taken out of the holiday money, our trip to the coast was now looking doomed. When Marge came around later for her elevenses I rattled out my grievances.

"Fancy buying a barbecue," I moaned, but Marge didn't have the same view.

"That party was a wonderful surprise for me and my Stan couldn't get over how generous you both are. He's a changed man. He's even talking about throwing a barbecue for everyone."

I was pleased for Marge, but what troubled me most was our summer holiday. The rate we were going we could just about afford two nights at a bed and breakfast — without the coach fare!

Stan came round the next morning to see if Jeff wanted to go up town to the shops — he'd quite enjoyed their little trip the day before.

An hour and a half later two proud men walked in the back door both holding a bunch of flowers. Was it a peace offering, I thought? Then, as I took my flowers from Jeff, I noticed the label: *Reduced*. I couldn't help but smile and neither could Marge when they announced they'd only bought three special offers each.

Later that afternoon, Ruth and Jessica called round with an invite to a granny and grandads' tea at her nursery school.

"You don't have to take anything, Granny," she said. "Can I have one of Grandad's buy one get one free biscuits, please?"

While I made the tea, Ruth went in the front room to have a word with her father, and returned a few minutes later informing me that I needed to stock up on the special offers as Jeff and Stan were planning a summer of barbecue parties.

My heart sank, and I realised I could probably say goodbye to our summer holiday this year.

Then, just as though Jessica sensed my plight, she climbed up on my lap and gave me a wet kiss on the cheek.

And as she tilted her head and smiled I counted my blessings and looked forward to a summer of parties, on the cheap. ■

Under The Gooseberry Bush

by Mary Clover.

M Y Caroline is a very sensible child — well, sensible enough for a five-year-old, that is. The only problem I ever have with her is that she does have an unfortunate tendency to fixate on things. You know how it is — her favourite doll was called Henrietta and she wanted the new baby to be a girl so that we could call her Henrietta, too.

But the fun really started when Jon's great-aunt Dot told Caroline that her daddy had found her underneath a gooseberry bush. This wasn't very helpful, especially as it resulted in lots of questions I didn't really want to answer, what with getting ready for the move and being six months pregnant at the time.

"But Mummy," my sensible daughter said, patting my fat tummy, "I thought the baby was growing inside you."

"Yes, that's right. And it's starting to get big now."

"So the baby is in there." Caroline patted my tummy again. Then she suddenly looked worried. "But you found me underneath a gooseberry bush?"

"No, no. You grew in my tummy, too," I reassured her. "You don't find babies under gooseberry bushes. Great-aunt Dot was just joking."

"Oh."

I gave Caroline a big hug. I could see there were still seeds of doubt in her pretty five-year-old head.

"And, anyway, we haven't got a gooseberry bush in the garden." That seemed to settle the matter for the time being.

As I said, Caroline was really quite a sensible child, and a helpful one, too. She packed her books and toys in some of the plastic crates the removal men had dropped off for us. I was a bit worried about the upheaval for her, because she would be starting at a new school. But she was looking forward to living in the country and, of course, to having her best friend to stay.

We were going from a house in town with a small garden, to a cottage on the edge of a village about ten miles away. The real plus point was the big garden there, which included a vegetable patch and a bed of soft fruit. There were even some fruit trees.

Jon, my husband, is the gardener in our family and he was already making plans for what he hoped to grow.

WE moved on a Friday. Caroline waved the big van off and kept her favourite doll to go with her in the car. We piled our essentials in the boot and set off, Caroline safely on her booster seat cuddling Henrietta.

The "Are we there yet?" questions started pretty quickly, so I was glad that it was quite a short journey. But, just before we got to the village, we passed a large poultry farm. Not that there was a hen in sight; they were inside the buildings that housed the batteries where they were kept.

Of course this meant I had to explain about hen batteries to Caroline. She said it was all wrong and that if she was a hen she wouldn't want to live in a cage. Quite so, and neither would I, but a five-year-old could hardly be expected to understand the economics of it all.

Anyway, as we were drawing up in front of our new home, a raucous honking noise greeted us. It was a pair of geese who waddled and flapped their way to the five-bar gate of the smallholding directly opposite, followed by a cockerel and some white hens. It was a dreadful racket.

I looked at Jon.

"We're living in the country now," I said, grinning.

"Do they honk all the time?" Caroline asked.

"I certainly hope not," Jon replied, looking a bit worried.

But this wasn't the moment to worry about geese. It was time to unload the car, get the kettle on and wait for the van.

Caroline ran in and out of the empty rooms and then out into the garden. Our van was just drawing up at the gate when she came running back in, all bright-eyed and excited.

"Mummy, there's a hen in the garden!"

"Well, we're not going to worry about it now, Caroline. It'll make its way home again soon enough when it's hungry. Come and give Daddy a hand with some of your toys."

AT the end of the day, when the removal men had gone, we left the chaos of the cottage and went out into the quiet of the garden. It was dusk already and the din from across the way had stopped now that all the birds had gone to sleep.

There was a sweet smell of blossom from the trees. We walked round the garden to see what was now ours.

Jon noted that the soft fruit would need attention — the bushes were unpruned and there were far too many weeds in that bed. Caroline wanted to know the names of the trees and bushes.

"Those are apple trees," Jon explained, "and that's a plum — a Victoria, I think."

"And what are the bushes?"

"Different kinds of currant, some raspberry canes, and it looks like a gooseberry at the back."

"Is that where you found me, Daddy?"

Oh, dear. Caroline hadn't forgotten what Great-aunt Dot had said, after all.

"We didn't live here then, did we?" Jon countered, putting his arm protectively round her shoulders.

✳   ✳   ✳   ✳

Thank heavens our first full day in our new home was a Saturday. We ached from moving furniture and unpacking boxes, and had promised ourselves a lie-in.

Unfortunately for us, we were awakened at six o'clock by loud crowing coming from the smallholding opposite. Jon drew back the curtains.

"There's a cockerel," he said crossly, "on the wall over there."

"Well, we are living in the country," I reminded him.

"Hmmph!" he muttered, rubbing the sleep from his eyes.

I sat down on the window seat beside him. The view was wonderful — all the way down the valley. We could also see into the yard of the smallholding. The noisy cockerel was lording it amongst his hens, and when an elderly lady came out to feed them all, he pushed the others out of the way to get the best of the food.

"I bet that cockerel's a real Lothario," Jon said with a chuckle.

"Daddy, what's a Lothario?"

Oh, dear. We hadn't heard Caroline come in. She was half asleep, Henrietta tucked firmly under her arm.

"Well, er . . ." Jon looked at me desperately. "It's a chap who has lots of girlfriends all at the same time and doesn't treat them very well."

"Oh," Caroline said, going pensive, "so he's a naughty cockerel, is he?"

We couldn't help laughing.

"Yes, he is," I told her. "Now let's get your clothes for today organised."

Herbal

Chamomile

YOU might mistake chamomile for a daisy and you'd be forgiven for doing so, as they both belong to the same plant family. The seemingly endless list of problems chamomile is said to help can all be traced to its effects on the nervous system and digestive system, as well as its anti-inflammatory properties.

Chamomile tea has a bittersweet flavour and stimulates the gastric juices. It's a wonderful herb for infants and is a favourite remedy for colic and digestive disorders.

Chamomile essential oil has a low toxicity level and has been used in medicinal preparations for over 250 years. Perhaps its soothing qualities are why chamomile was believed to attract prosperity and love, and its tiny flowers were thought to be enjoyed by flower fairies!

AS soon as she was dressed, Caroline went outside. I thought she'd run straight over to the smallholding to see the geese and hens and the naughty cockerel. But as I watched from the kitchen window, she made straight for the fruit bushes. She prowled around, sometimes disappearing from view, and then came racing back into the house, excited and breathless.

"Mummy, there's a hen under the gooseberry bush!" She grabbed my hand and led me out to the garden.

"See," she whispered, pointing.

And there, indeed, was a hen, sitting on a patch of scratched earth under the gooseberry bush. It was a rather sad, scrawny-looking hen, with a droopy comb and reddish-brown feathers. As soon as it became aware of our presence, it blinked and scuttled off.

"See, Mummy — it was a hen. And it's not like the ones over there." She pointed across the way.

"Yes, you're right, Caro," I said. "But it will go back to its own home now.

Know-how!

It was just visiting us."

Her face fell, so I put my arm around her to console her.

"Or it might be looking for food."

Caroline's soft heart went out to the hen. She thought it all wrong that the hen had to go off and look for food when it wanted to live in our garden. So she took out some muesli in a cereal bowl and we cut an old plastic bottle down to make a bowl for water.

Caroline placed the bowls carefully under the gooseberry bush and waited, but nothing happened.

"The hen is probably shy," I explained. "We've got to gain its confidence. Come in and have your breakfast now and we can check on the hen later."

Caroline was in her pyjamas when she checked the gooseberry bush for the last time that day. She reported back that the hen had drunk most of the water and eaten some of the muesli, and now it had gone to sleep. She topped up the water and went to bed, feeling pleased that she and the hen were making progress.

THIS routine continued for a couple of weeks. The hen started to grow confident and I would see it pecking round the garden, though the gooseberry bush remained its favourite place. Sometimes it strayed into the field or down the lane, but it always came back.

It was putting on weight, and the reddish-brown feathers were looking sleeker. It was amazing how quickly it had become an established part of our little family.

"I'm going to call her Henna," Caroline announced, "because she's a hen and her feathers are the same colour as your hair."

"And I put henna on my hair?"

"That's right," she said solemnly. "I've seen you with the bottle and it says *henna* on it."

That made me laugh. There was no hiding anything from this child.

Luckily, Caroline settled in well at the village school and soon had a new best friend, Megan. And I got on really well with Megan's mum, Sarah. We

63

met at the school gate and soon became friends ourselves.

They farmed on the other side of the village, mainly sheep, and it turned out that our garden backed on to their top field. Sarah kept a few bantams for pin money and she was the one who told me that Henna was most probably a Rhode Island Red that had escaped from the large poultry farm up the road.

Of course, Jon rang the poultry farm immediately, but the manager wasn't very interested in one hen that might have gone missing weeks before.

"So we can keep Henna?" Caroline implored Jon, throwing her arms round her daddy and giving him a big kiss.

"Well, it looks like it."

NOT long afterwards, Caroline got her reward. On the bare earth, underneath the gooseberry bush, she found one big brown egg.

"Oh, Henna's laid you your breakfast!" I exclaimed when she brought it in to show me. I crouched down to her height. "Now you've seen what tender loving care can do."

I planted a soft kiss on her forehead.

"Henna's saying 'thank you' for you having a heart of gold."

"Is it really gold?" Caroline asked, furrowing her brow and looking worried.

I had to laugh.

"No, Caro, that's just what people say. It means you're a really nice person."

We had an egg a day for about a week. Caroline was on cloud nine. Then one morning she came into the kitchen nearly in tears.

"Henna pecked me." She showed me the red marks on her hand and forearm.

"Oh, that's nothing," I said to reassure her as I rubbed some lotion in. "Maybe you gave her a bit of a fright or something."

But, actually, I did feel a bit worried because I had noticed that Henna's behaviour was changing. Whenever she saw me or Caroline or Jon she scuttled off through the hole in the hedge. The bare patch under the gooseberry bush even started to sprout grass because she wasn't there as often.

Caroline was very sad about Henna's disappearances. And then Megan told her that the fox had got some of their bantams. To be honest, Sarah had rung me about this but I hadn't wanted to upset Caroline even more by passing on this news.

"I think the fox has got Henna," Caroline whispered to me when Henna had been missing for two weeks. "I found two of her feathers by the hole in the hedge."

"Just two?" I queried, and Caroline nodded, the tears trickling down her cheeks. I gave her a cuddle and felt quite lost. I just didn't know what to say.

The reception teacher noticed that there was something wrong and phoned me to ask, as tactfully as she could, if there had been a family bereavement. Whatever it was had started affecting Caroline's schoolwork — and she had been getting on so well with her reading.

I also noted that she had started carrying Henrietta round all the time again when she was at home.

By now I had to admit that my hen psychology was wearing a bit thin. We didn't know where Henna had got to, or even if she was still alive. Even contemplating the worst brought a lump to my throat, too. Would you ever believe that a hen could arouse such depth of emotion?

Jon and I tried to look on the bright side for Caroline's sake. I explained that Henna wanted to be independent, and that that was a good thing.

"After all, if she relies on us for food all the time, she will never be able to cope if we go away."

"But I don't want to go away," Caroline said crossly, sounding just like her dad when he was grumpy. "I want to be with Henna."

Then she gripped Henrietta tightly under her arm and went upstairs to her bedroom.

We seemed to have reached an impasse. I was almost hoping that the baby would come early to take Caroline's mind off Henna — not to mention the fact that I was reaching the "wish it was all over" stage.

The heatwave wasn't helping, either. My ankles were swollen and I had to lie with my feet up on the sun-lounger in the afternoons.

Sarah was marvellous. She started bringing Caroline home after school each day. Sometimes she would drive, but a couple of times they took the shortcut across the fields. There was a footpath there and, as Sarah pointed out, it was their land after all.

O N the first day back after half-term, Sarah rang to ask if Caroline could play with Megan after school, because her car was being serviced.

"Then they can walk back together across the fields and I'll pick Megan up when I've got the car back."

My heart did a somersault. Well, wouldn't any mother worry?

"Oh, there's nothing to worry about." Sarah must have read my thoughts down the phone line. "They'll be perfectly all right and Floss will be with them. She won't let them stray."

Of course — Floss, their collie. That was some reassurance. Even so, I couldn't really settle to reading or doing the crossword when I had my feet up on the lounger outside. But I must have dozed off because, the next thing I knew, Caroline was pulling excitedly at my arm.

"Mummy, Mummy. Henna's had some babies."

Babies? Hens don't have babies. But Caroline was pulling at me, and Megan was nodding and pointing in the direction of the field. Floss stretched out, panting, in the shade of the lounger.

"Caro, go and get Floss some water," I said.

She quickly filled a plastic bowl from the outside tap and ran back to me.

"Come on, Mummy," she pleaded. "You've got to come."

She and Megan took my hands and led me out of the garden and along the lane. The geese honked at us and the cockerel was crowing from his vantage point on the wall. It was funny, but we didn't even notice the noise from the smallholding now.

The girls stopped at the stile.

"I'm not climbing over that!" I said firmly.

"But you don't have to. Look, Mummy!" Caroline clambered on to the stile and pointed.

AND there, making her way to the hole in our hedge, was Henna. She clucked with pride as she escorted three chicks that were just coming out of the fluffy stage.

"Good heavens!" I gasped.

"We found Henna in a new nest," Caroline explained breathlessly.

"Behind the sheep shelter," Megan added.

"And Henna was really, really happy to see me." Caroline was overjoyed.

"That's because she's a proud mum." I put my arm round Caroline's little shoulders.

"The cockerel was very naughty, wasn't he, Mummy?" Caroline smiled up at me, knowingly. "Just like Daddy said."

I couldn't help laughing to myself.

"Yes, you're right, Caro," I said, making a mental note never again to underestimate the sharpness of a bright five-year-old.

We walked back home, Megan running on ahead of us, and I told Caroline my news.

"We had a letter from Great-aunt Dot this morning and guess what?"

"Is she coming to stay?" Caroline clapped her hands. She adored Great-aunt Dot, mainly because she spoiled her dreadfully.

"Yes, and you'll be able to show her Henna's gooseberry bush, won't you?"

"Oh, yes," Caroline agreed. "But, Mummy, I'll tell her that you don't find babies there, because I don't think she knows."

Now you may not believe me, but I swear next-door's cockerel winked at me as we went past, happily making our way home. ∎

River Eske, Co. Donegal

WE recently enjoyed a coach trip to Donegal. We had a super view over Donegal Bay from our bedroom and could watch the waterbus going in and out.

There was a colony of seals and also a very friendly dolphin in the bay, which made the newspaper headlines!

We didn't have time to see all the sights, but did get to Killybegs and to the castle in the Genveagh National Park.

— *Mr & Mrs T.R., Notts.*

J. CAMPBELL KERR.

The Anniversary Surprise

ROSIE pulled up the kitchen blind to reveal a dazzling summer morning. This was always the best time of year in her garden. The grass was at its greenest, the flowers at their brightest and — there was a dirty great, bright blue lump smack bang in the middle of the lawn!

"What —?"

Suddenly the blind dropped and she turned to see Sam grinning all over his face.

"Sam —" she began.

"I know what you're going to say," he broke in, still grinning infuriatingly.

"But I want you to trust me. There's nothing to worry about."

If ever there were two sentences designed to strike trepidation, Sam had just uttered them. Usually when people asked you to trust them, it was because they were up to something.

And if they said there was nothing to worry about, it usually meant that there was.

"Honestly, love," he went on, unperturbed by her sceptical look. "It's just . . . a surprise for our tenth wedding anniversary. You do think ten years should be celebrated, don't you?"

"Yes, but . . ."

"Promise me you won't look under the tarpaulin," he said.

"But —"

"Promise?"

by Teresa Ashby.

68

How could she resist that mischievous grin, those dancing blue eyes? All the same . . . whatever it was, it was big, and she was worried about the grass beneath.

If that object stayed there for too long, when it was moved the grass would have yellowed. Their anniversary was a week away. Would her lawn be all right for a week? And when all was finally revealed, where was she going to put it?

"All right." She sighed. "I promise."

"And I have witnesses," Sam said.

Their three children were lined up behind them. Even Alfie, at just over a year old, seemed to understand.

Sam opened the blind again and this time when Rosie looked, the blue lump seemed to have grown.

"What's under there, Sam?" she demanded. "An elephant?"

"Don't look," he repeated. "You promised. I want it to be a surprise and I haven't quite finished it yet."

"Is it something you've made?" she asked.

"It's more like ingredients," he said cryptically.

"Ingredients!" Rosie cried. "You mean there's more?"

She thought of the jumper she was knitting for him. She wasn't the world's fastest knitter, and she'd had a bit of help from her mum, but it had taken her weeks.

She'd been very proud of it, too, until she saw what was lurking in the back garden.

Illustration by Gerard Fay.

"DO you know what's under there?" she asked Sara and Jamie at lunch.

She could see from their secret smiles and dimpled cheeks that they knew very well what it was.

"They won't tell," Sam assured her. "They've been sworn to secrecy."

"And you mustn't look, Mummy," Sara said with a very grown-up frown on her six-year-old face. "It's a surprise."

It was out there — calling to her. Now she knew how all those fairytale heroines felt when told not to look behind the mysterious locked door.

It wasn't her fault. Every time she looked out of the kitchen window it tormented her. She couldn't peel a potato, wash up a cup or fill the kettle without "the thing" catching her eye.

And hanging out her washing every day was torture, because she had to stand quite near it. To be so close and not allowed even a little peek!

BY Thursday, Rosie was itching to lift up the tarpaulin and see what was beneath, but she'd made a promise and she couldn't break it, even if little Alfie was the only witness, with Sam at work and Sara and Jamie at school.

She pegged a shirt on the line.

"No, Alfie," Rosie said sternly as he toddled drunkenly towards the mystery object.

He looked at her, his face starting to crumple as he lost his balance and sat down on the grass. He hated the word "no". It was all he'd seemed to hear since he'd learned to walk on his own.

She pegged out another shirt as Alfie hauled himself back to his feet and set off again towards the tarpaulin. After all the effort of getting back on his feet, she didn't want to distract him.

It wouldn't hurt to let him wander over to the object. It wasn't as if Sam would have left anything dangerous in the garden.

Alfie bent down, caught up the corner of the tarpaulin and lifted it up with a gleeful giggle.

"Bo!" he said, dropping it down. Then he lifted it up again.

"Bo!" he repeated, and dropped it down.

"Peep-bo!" Rosie laughed. "Are you playing hide-and-seek with me?"

For a moment, she forgot that the tarpaulin was there to hide something. She stopped pegging out the washing and joined in the game, pretending to be startled every time Alfie yelled.

Finally, breathless from giggling, Alfie plopped down on the grass and began to pluck at the daisies in the lawn.

Rosie sat down, too. It was then that she noticed the tarpaulin was still caught up and she could see something beneath it. Something wooden.

"Bo!" Alfie screwed his face up with concentration as he always did when trying out a new word.

"Bo, bo, bo — boat!"

Well, I didn't look, Rosie told herself afterwards. It wasn't my fault that Alfie left the tarpaulin slightly caught up and I saw the boat.

And — Alfie had told her what it was. Closer inspection revealed an upside-down boat — which didn't seem to be in particularly good condition. She covered it back up.

That afternoon she paced the kitchen floor wondering whether to tell Sam now to get rid of it, or wait until Sunday, and completely ruin his surprise.

What a dreadful position to be in! But what was he thinking? He knew she didn't like boats. She didn't mind swimming, or sitting watching the water, but being out on it was another matter entirely.

Sam should know. The one and only time they'd gone out on a small boat for an afternoon, it had been awful. She had felt so ill, despite the water being almost flat, and she'd got badly sunburned, not realising how exposed she'd been.

It was a long time ago, of course — before they were married. Perhaps she'd be all right in a boat now. And, of course, she'd remember to cover up or use a lot of sun-cream if she went out on the water these days.

She bit her lip. She would just have to pretend to know nothing about the boat and act surprised and delighted when he unveiled it on Sunday.

Perhaps, if she pretended hard enough, she really would grow to like it. Wasn't that what marriage was all about? Compromise?

If Sam didn't like the jumper she'd knitted him, he'd wear it anyway, because he loved her. If their tenth wedding anniversary wasn't about loving each other, then what was it about?

"What are you smiling about?" Sam asked when he came in.

"Just thinking how much I love you," she said.

O N Saturday Sam disappeared for much of the afternoon.

"He's gone on a mission," Jamie said.

"To get the rest of your present," Sara added, and Jamie shushed her.

The rest of it? Could it be oars? Rosie giggled. Life-jackets? She might need one if she fell overboard.

"Why are you laughing, Mummy?" Sara asked.

"I'm just happy, sweetheart," she fibbed.

Well, it was almost true. She would have been perfectly happy if it hadn't been for that dilemma in the garden.

Sam returned from his trip and spent ages clattering about in the garage, then he stuck his head round the door.

"Don't look in the garage, OK?"

It hadn't been easy knitting a Sam-sized jumper without him noticing — having to hide it all away when he came in unexpectedly. She'd dropped a few stitches along the way, which had to be rescued and put right again by her mother. But as she wrapped the finished article, Rosie felt a swell of pride. There was love woven into every stitch. It could last him a lifetime. He'd be able to wear it when they went out on the boat.

She smiled and pushed back the fears that kept rising up despite repeatedly telling herself that it would be OK.

✳   ✳   ✳   ✳

On Sunday morning Rosie woke to find herself alone in the bed. It was very early. Much earlier than they usually got up, even during the week! Sam must be bringing her breakfast in bed, she decided and, turning over, settled back to sleep with a smile on her face.

She had a nightmare. She dreamed they were out on the boat. It had sprung a leak and she was desperately trying to bale out with her Thermos flask.

Summer Cat

J. Winkley.

"It's all right," Sam said equably. "We can row to shore."

"But you forgot the oars, Sam!" Rosie cried.

There was no logic to it. They were in the middle of a turquoise sea, fins of sharks circling around them.

"At least the children are safe," she said in her dream.

"Are they?" Sam asked and when she looked behind her, the three children were sitting in a line with their life-jackets on.

"Mummy!" Sara shrieked. "Mummy! Come on!"

"I'm going as fast as I can." Rosie flapped, scooping up water in her Thermos and chucking it over the side.

"Hurry up, Mum!" Jamie yelled, shaking her arm so that she spilled the water back in the boat.

"Mamma," Alfie wailed. "Boat!"

＊　　＊　　＊　　＊

Rosie opened her eyes with a start and almost burst into tears of relief to find herself in her own bed with the children sitting all around her and Sam holding her breakfast tray.

"What were you dreaming about?" He laughed. "You were waving your arms around and muttering about going as fast as you could. Were you driving a racing car?"

Her mouth felt dry. It was no use. She really was scared of boats and somehow she'd have to tell him. He loved her. He'd understand.

She sat up and he placed the tray on her lap. It had everything — a cup of tea, a bud vase with a single red rose in it, still with morning dew on the petals, and crisp golden toast with lime marmalade.

When she'd finished, she gave Sam his parcel, and the delight on his face when he saw the jumper was wonderful.

"Do you like it?"

"I love it," he said. "Did your mother knit it for me?"

"No," Rosie replied, her voice trembling slightly. "I did."

"You did this? It's fantastic!"

He pulled it on and it was a perfect fit.

"It took Mummy ages," Sara said.

"I'm sure it did." Sam smiled. "Thank you, darling. It's the most perfect

72

MY cat is enjoying the sun on her fur,
It makes her warm and it makes
her purr.
She's smiling up towards the sky,
She breathes a small, contented sigh;
Glad of summer, glad of heat
To warm her dainty, fuzzy feet.
Moving from the sun to shade,
Into shadows things have made,
Glad of breezes passing by;
Peeping at the ones who fly.
Then, as hottest rays descend,
And time moves on towards day's end,
She's back into the evening light
To warm soft fur before the night.

— *Enid Pearson.*

present I've ever had — and all the more special because you made it for me."

"Well," Rosie said. "Am I going to see what's under that tarpaulin at last?"

"Come over to the window," Sam said.

Jamie stood on one side of the window, Sara on the other. Sam scooped Alfie up and held him on his hip, then put the other arm round Rosie.

"Close your eyes, love."

She closed them tightly.

"Open the curtains, kids," Sam said.

She heard the swish of the curtains and felt a tremor of excitement, even though she knew what to expect when she opened her eyes.

The suspense was killing her.

"Surprise!" the children yelled.

It certainly was!

"Sam!" Rosie gasped. "I can't believe it. Did you do that?"

"I had some help," he said, winking at the children. "We were up at the crack of dawn."

"You must have been," she said. "Oh, Sam, it's wonderful."

THERE was no sign of the tarpaulin and the boat had been moved from the middle of the lawn to the back, where it had been placed at an angle.

"Michael came over and helped me shift it into position early this morning," Sam told her.

"My brother? Up early on a Sunday?"

Not only had the boat been moved, it had been filled with earth and planted with all manner of flowers and trailing plants.

"I had no idea," Rosie breathed, and it was true. It looked beautiful — and such an unusual garden feature. A raised bed — but from a boat.

She turned and hugged Sam, who was still holding Alfie, then drew Jamie and Sara into the embrace.

"I'm so lucky." Rosie felt suddenly tearful and very relieved.

"We're the lucky ones," Sam said, his voice a little hoarse.

All Rosie's worries had been for nothing. The old boat's days on the water were well over. Now it served a much nicer purpose.

She reached up and kissed Sam. He had been telling the truth when he said there was nothing to worry about. She would remember that in future and, as long as she did, she knew they'd be all right. ■

I Should Be So Lucky!

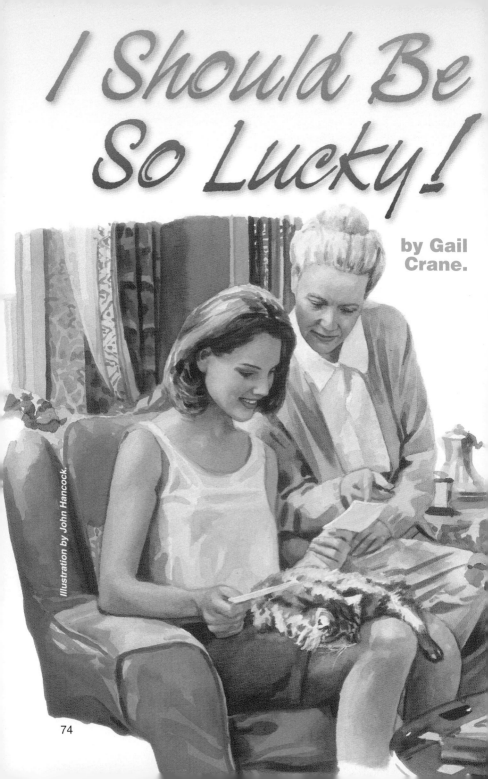

by Gail Crane.

Illustration by John Hancock.

74

I'VE always been superstitious.

If I spill the salt, I immediately throw a good pinch over my shoulder. I cross the road to avoid walking under a ladder, and I never, never make any decisions or take any risks on Friday the thirteenth. In fact, I would happily stay in bed all day, if it were possible, rather than face the consequences of a careless action on that inauspicious date.

So you can imagine my horror at the train of events that began in the bathroom that dreadful morning . . .

✳   ✳   ✳   ✳

I'm engaged to be married to the most wonderful man in the world. I think he must also be one of the most tolerant!

The first time I went out with Mike, I inadvertently put my jacket on inside out — that was the effect he had on me, even then. When he pointed out what I'd done I refused to turn it the right way out. That would have been terribly unlucky, and there was no way I was going to risk jeopardising our relationship, because I knew, even then, that this was the man for me.

In the end I compromised by taking off my jacket and carrying it, despite it being a chilly autumn evening. Mike found it highly amusing, although he probably also thought me quite mad.

Luckily, he continued over time to find my "eccentricity", as he called it, endearing, and our relationship thrived. Within six months we were engaged, and six months after that we were preparing to walk down the aisle.

The reception was booked, the cake baked and the flowers ordered. I had found the most wonderful dress in a small boutique in town, and I was going to wear the same veil my mother had worn at her wedding twenty-seven years ago. "Something new and something borrowed"; I still had to find something old and something blue.

I was particularly touched by my brother Stephen's wedding present. From goodness knows where he had managed to find a real chimney sweep, who had agreed to appear at the church and pose for some of the photographs!

Life was wonderful. I was walking on air and had never been so happy.

Then, one morning, I turned quickly in the bathroom and knocked the mirror off the window-sill. It was like a bad dream. I could see the mirror falling and made a grab for it, but I couldn't move fast enough. I watched in horror as it bounced off the side of the bath and crashed to the floor in a thousand tiny pieces.

Seven years of bad luck!

"Whatever is the matter, Gill?"

My mother must have heard the crash, and my cry of dismay.

"It's only a mirror," she soothed, hugging me. "It's not the end of the world."

But to me, at that moment, it felt exactly that. Especially as the pretty silver-framed mirror had been a present to Mum from Dad on their twenty-fifth wedding anniversary. I felt awful.

"I'm so sorry, Mum."

She picked it up from the floor.

"Look, I don't think the frame has been damaged at all," she said. "Perhaps we can have some new glass put in?"

I realised I could ask Mike to take it to the silversmith at the small engineering and craft centre in the next village, as he had to drive past it on his way to work. I decided I'd give it to him when I saw him that evening.

Then it began to rain. After the episode with the mirror, I was already late for work. Rushing, I threw on my coat, picked up my bag and rummaged on the coat stand for my umbrella. It's a spring-loaded one that opens automatically when the button is pressed, and somehow, I must have caught it accidentally. Suddenly there it was, open — inside the house! This day was going from bad to worse.

To add insult to injury, as I walked out to the car a solitary magpie settled on the bonnet and squawked at me.

"One for sorrow! One for sorrow!" he seemed to be saying.

"You don't have to rub it in!" I shouted, slamming the car door shut.

TWO days later, Mike heard that he was to be made redundant. Of course, I wasn't really surprised. I had been expecting bad news, what with the mirror, the umbrella and the magpie all in the one morning.

"Don't be silly, Gill," Mike said. "We've known for some time that this was on the cards. With the company having to downsize it was inevitable that one of the engineers would have to go. I was the last one in, so it followed that I'd be the first one out. I'll find something else — don't worry."

"Suppose we have seven years' bad luck, what will happen then? How can we get married if you don't have a job? We can't live on what I earn!"

"Gill, you have to stop this. It's getting ridiculous." I could tell that Mike was getting cross, and who could blame him? It *was* ridiculous, but I couldn't help myself.

"I've already been looking round for another job," he reassured me. "Something will turn up, you'll see."

That weekend, I went to see Gran.

Dear Gran, she had always been there for both Mike and me when we needed her, and just now, I really did need someone to talk to.

"You must have faith in Mike," she told me after I had related the whole sorry tale and had a good sob into the bargain. "He's a clever lad, and I'm sure he'll soon find something. And if he doesn't, then you will still manage.

So long as you love each other you can cope with anything."

She gave me a hug.

"Now, dry your eyes. I've got something to show you."

She took a cardboard box from the cupboard under the stairs and put it on the coffee table in front of us. It was tied with yellow ribbon.

"This is from my wedding bouquet," she murmured, stroking the faded ribbon lovingly. "Of course, it wasn't a big one, just a few chrysanths from Dad's garden. It was the end of the Depression, and there was no spare money for grand weddings. I wore my best frock, and a straw hat that Mother had trimmed with more flowers."

I watched, fascinated, as she opened the box. I had never been shown this before.

She gently laid the lid to one side next to the ribbon, and took out a small album.

YOUR great-uncle George took these," she said. "Somehow he managed to borrow a camera from a friend, and this was his wedding present to us."

The grey pages were faded with age, and the photos themselves were tiny. As I turned the leaves, I could see Grandad in his best suit standing next to Gran, who looked radiant in her wedding outfit, holding her bunch of home-grown flowers. They both seemed so happy.

"Your grandad was out of work then, as a lot of men were at that time, but we decided to go ahead and get married anyway. We loved each other too much to wait, so we lived with his parents for a while until he eventually found a job."

I reached out and squeezed Gran's hand, touched that she had chosen now to share this with me.

She reached into the box again and lifted out a small tissue-wrapped package.

"This was the one thing I had that was new. My sisters must have saved from their wages for weeks to buy it for me!" She smiled and handed it to me. "I would like you to have it for your wedding."

My hand trembled as I took it. I guessed that, whatever it was, it must be very precious to Gran. Carefully, I unfolded the paper. I could hardly believe my eyes when I saw what it contained. Lying on the crumpled tissue was the most beautiful blue lace garter, threaded with delicate ribbon in a paler shade of blue.

"It's gorgeous, Gran," I whispered, gently stroking the intricate pattern of the lace. "Thank you so much."

"There's something else." Gran reached once more into her box of treasures and handed me another small package. It was a tiny fold of paper, yellowed and brittle with age.

"Open it," she urged.

Carefully, I unfolded the fragile leaves of paper to reveal a small silver coin, unlike any I had seen before. I looked up at her questioningly.

"It's a sixpence," she said. "A silver sixpence."

I had no idea why Gran was giving me this, although it clearly had some deep significance for her. My puzzlement must have been obvious, for she reached out and placed the coin in the palm of my hand.

"There is an old belief," she explained, "that if a bride slips a silver sixpence into her shoe on her wedding day it will bring her good luck and prosperity."

"Did you . . .?" I began.

"I did — this very one. And, as you know, your grandad was eventually able to set up his own business and we had a wonderful life together."

I studied the coin in my hand. It seemed very old.

"Do you think that if I were to . . ." I left the question unfinished.

"Who knows? There is one thing you have to remember, though."

I looked at her questioningly.

"It has to be a secret. You must not tell anyone or it won't work."

I closed my hand around the sixpence and squeezed it tightly. With my other hand I touched the garter.

"Something old and something blue."

Herbal

Bilberry

BILBERRY, a close relative of the cranberry and blueberry, was widely used in days gone by. The fruit and leaves were both prized, but it was the berries that were found to be the most effective.

Strangely enough, one of their uses — for eyecare and vision — has been proven by modern medicine to be absolutely accurate. Macular degeneration and other age-related eye diseases are often caused by a breakdown of the circulatory system of the eye. Bilberry fruits have been proven to strengthen and protect capillaries and improve circulation, making them excellent at fighting these eye problems.

Isn't it strange how often ancient medicines turn out to be good at curing modern health problems, too? Perhaps those herbalists of long ago deserve an overdue thank you from all of us!

MIKE had so far had no luck finding a job, despite all the application letters he had written, and his redundancy notice period would end two weeks after we returned from our honeymoon. Curiously, I was now unworried by this lack of progress. Ever since my talk with Gran, I had felt a strange confidence that things would turn out all right.

I stood in front of my bedroom mirror on the morning of the wedding, waiting for Dad to escort me out to the car. Gran's blue garter was safely in place above my left knee, and Mum's veil hung in delicate folds across my face.

78

know-how!

I had one last thing to do before I left.

Carefully, I took the silver sixpence from its paper wrapping. For a moment I held it, thinking of Gran on her wedding day. I sent her a silent thank you.

Then I slipped off my shoe, dropped the coin in and replaced the shoe on my foot.

Ouch! Ah, well. What was a little discomfort in the interests of good luck?

I MADE my way down the aisle, hoping that no-one would notice my slightly irregular gait, and limped through the reception.

"You really should have worn those shoes in better," the bridesmaid, my old friend Anne-Marie, commented. "Why don't you go upstairs and change them? It's not as if anybody's going to notice now."

But I was determined that coin would stay put if it killed me! However, I couldn't deny it was a relief when the time came to get ready to leave for the honeymoon and I knew I could finally take it out of my shoe!

As we were going up the stairs to change, Mike's father called to him and passed him an envelope.

"This came just after you left for the church," he explained. "I quite forgot about it till now."

"Thanks, Dad."

*　　*　　*　　*

"I suppose I had better open it," Mike said upstairs, sitting on the edge of the bed. "You never know, it might be something important."

I was slipping out of my wedding dress when he gave a whoop of delight.

"Yes!" He grabbed me round the waist and hugged me.

"Mind the dress," I protested half-heartedly, eventually managing to throw it safely across a chair.

"I've got it," Mike announced, giving me a resounding kiss. "I've got a job!"

79

"Oh, Mike, that's wonderful." I hugged him ecstatically and kissed him back. "Well done!"

With a sigh of relief I kicked off my shoes and picked up the sixpence as it rolled on to the floor. It was a miracle! I could hardly believe it, but it had worked.

"What on earth is that?"

I pulled Mike down to sit beside me and explained about Gran's gifts, and how I'd hoped the sixpence would somehow cancel out the bad luck of the broken mirror.

"You goose," he said affectionately. "Am I ever going to cure you of this obsession with superstition?"

"But it worked, didn't it?" I challenged. "You have to admit it. You have the evidence there in your hand." I pointed to the letter.

"Gill, my love, listen to me."

HE put one arm round my shoulders and held me close. "This job," he began, "is something that I knew about long before you went to see your gran. Do you remember the day you broke the mirror?"

How could I forget? But what had that to do with Mike's job?

"Well," he continued, "I took the frame to the silversmith as you asked and, while I was there, I got talking to the owner of the centre. Turns out he was looking for a maintenance engineer for some of the equipment they've installed in the light industrial units. They don't have anyone on the staff that they can spare. Well, he offered me the job.

"I didn't say anything at the time because he had to discuss it with his fellow directors, and I didn't want to get your hopes up and then have to disappoint you. The letter that came today is just confirming the appointment."

He put a hand on each of my shoulders and turned me round to face him.

"So you see, my superstitious wife, it has nothing whatsoever to do with silver sixpences. In fact," he added, "what we really have to thank for getting me the job is the broken mirror. That mirror you were convinced was going to bring us bad luck has actually turned out to be very lucky indeed!"

Although it went against everything I believed in, I had to admit that it certainly did look that way.

Nevertheless, I wrapped the silver sixpence carefully in its paper and put it away safely with the garter. After all, I thought, I never knew when I might need it again.

Oh, yes. As we were getting into the car to drive away on our honeymoon, two magpies settled on the fence next to us.

Mike and I looked at each other and laughed.

"Two for joy." Maybe that's one superstition Mike will believe in! ■

By Any Other Name

THE one thing I would never ever be, I always said, was a gardener. There were quite enough of those in our family already, believe me!

A great-great-aunt had traipsed all over Tibet on a donkey looking for rare specimens — she even had one weedy little plant named after her. Gran was obsessed with anything that grew, but especially loved the clematis which wreathed and twined over every post, trellis and wall in her garden.

My mum, on the other hand, was nutty over old-fashioned roses — which explains my rather unusual name. While my future school friends were being named Emily, Charlotte and Sara, I was held over the font in our village church to be christened Albertine. Apparently I screamed my head off. With that name, I'm not surprised.

Illustration by David Young.

by Polly Weston.

81

Anyway, as I said, I was determined that I was not going to follow in their green-fingered footsteps, if you see what I mean.

That is, until that sunny Sunday afternoon in June . . .

It was Gran's birthday, and when Mum asked what she would like to do she knew exactly where she wanted to go.

Belmont Manor was a Victorian mansion that had recently been rescued from decay by a trust. They had just begun work on the gardens, which were being opened to the public at weekends to help raise funds.

I left them exclaiming over the old rose garden — I could see several of my namesakes — and wandered off round the lake. When I returned, they were in earnest conversation with a tall young man.

A S I came up to them he turned and I fell hopelessly in love. He was a combination of Mr Darcy and Mr Rochester; black curls, brown eyes, tanned skin — my sixteen-year-old insides melted.

"Ah," Mum said, "here's my daughter . . ."

"Allie," I put in quickly. I didn't want him to know my embarrassing name.

"This is Steven, love. He's the head gardener here."

He smiled down at me.

"And is she an expert on old roses, too?"

Just then his mobile phone rang. He answered it, spoke for a moment and then smiled.

"Sorry about that, but I'm wanted in the office. Nice to talk to you." And with a quick wave, he had gone.

For the rest of that day I was in a happy daze, but then reality kicked in. After all, I could hardly go back to the manor every weekend. How was I ever going to see him again?

*   *   *   *

Our form teacher, who was a Miss Jean Brodie clone, liked her girls — it was an all-girls school — to start thinking about their future careers. So, at the end of the summer term, once the exams were over, we were expected to spend a fortnight out of school on work experience.

For several weeks I'd been trying to ignore the long list of possible jobs pinned up on our noticeboard, but on Monday morning I went in early. I checked the list, then waited for Miss Garvey to appear.

"Good morning, Albertine." No nonsense with Allie here.

"Morning, Miss Garvey. That gardening work experience — I'd like to put my name down for it."

"At Belmont?" She gave me a long look over her spectacles. "But last week, when I suggested it, you said you'd had enough gardening to last you two lifetimes."

"Yes, well . . ." I had the grace to blush. "I've had second thoughts since then."

She still didn't look convinced, but she finally put my name down on the list and gave me Belmont's telephone number and directions.

A COUPLE of weeks later, clad in my most fetching shorts and T-shirt and carrying the new green gardener's apron which Gran had given me, I arrived well ahead of time at Belmont. An arrow directed me to the office and, through the open door, I saw Steven working at a desk, looking more gorgeous than ever.

He looked up.

"Yes? Can I help you?"

I cleared my throat.

"I'm from the high school. I've come to help."

"Oh, right. Come in then. Take a pew. I've seen you before, haven't I?"

"Yes, on a visit here. You were talking to my mum and gran."

"Ah, of course. So you're a keen gardener, too?"

"Oh, yes." What lovely long eyelashes he had. He was even better-looking close up, too!

I watched as he drew a blank name tag towards him.

"Name?"

"Allie Adams."

"Short for Alison, is it?" He paused, marker pen in hand.

"No, not exactly."

"Well, what then?"

"Albertine," I muttered, looking down at my new trainers.

"That's original." Steven smiled. "Your mother's choice, of course."

"Yes, she wanted me to be Albertine Mermaid Honorine, after her three favourite roses, but Gran persuaded her to drop the Mermaid."

"Mmm, pity. It's a glorious rose." His eyes twinkled. "Still, look on the bright side. If you'd been a boy, you could have ended up as Parkdirektor Riggers Adams."

Even I could see the funny side of that.

I heard a step behind me then and turned to see a chunky, fair-haired young man in faded denims and T-shirt, clutching a motorbike helmet.

"Hi, Steven. Sorry I'm late. I had problems starting the bike."

"That's OK, Rob. This is Allie. She's here from the high school for a couple of weeks' work experience."

"Oh, right." Rob barely deigned to glance at me. "I'll get on with the pruning then, shall I?"

"Fine. Rob's in his first year at the local horticultural college," Steven added for my benefit. "He's here for the summer."

He handed me my name tag.

"Now, what are we going to find for you to do? You've done quite a bit of garden work at home, I expect?"

I thought briefly of all the times I'd been forced into helping in our garden. I wasn't sure I could really remember anything I'd done.

"I could do some pruning," I said, desperate to have Steven think I was good at something.

"Have you ever done any?"

"Well, I've seen Mum do it often enough."

"Allie's mum and gran are brilliant gardeners," Steven told Rob.

"Really?" Rob favoured me with a rather sardonic look and I had a nasty feeling that he saw right through me.

"I think before we let you loose on anything major, you can do some weeding today. That way I can see how you shape up. We're returning the old walled garden to a vegetable plot and it needs a good bit of attention."

✳   ✳   ✳   ✳

I straightened my aching back. It was hard work, this gardening lark. In fact, I was only sticking it out because I knew that in the end Steven would look up and suddenly see me quite differently — like Mr Darcy spotting Lizzie across a crowded ballroom. At least he'd be pleased with me today, which was a start.

"What on earth have you been up to?"

I jumped out of my rose-tinted dream and swung round to face Rob.

"What do you mean, what have I been up to?" I demanded indignantly. "Weeding, of course, like Steven told me."

"But he didn't tell you to pull those up!" He pointed to the row of upended dandelion plants.

"But I'd finished weeding the rows of carrots." I didn't tell him that I'd carefully replanted all the ones I'd accidentally dug up. "So I decided to dig up the dandelions. They were nearly setting seed. You know the saying — one year's seeds, seven years' weeds."

Rob rolled his eyes in mock horror.

"Those dandelions were being cultivated. The Victorians used them as salad plants."

"No! Really?"

"What on earth have you been up to?'

It was Steven this time who'd come up behind me.

"I'm sorry. I didn't realise you actually grew dandelions."

"Well, we do. And what's wrong with those carrots?"

I saw that the ones I'd hastily pushed back in were drooping alarmingly in the sun.

"It's the heat, I expect," Rob said. "Why don't I get some water for them?"

"Yes, you'd better," was all that Steven said, but he was still eyeing me thoughtfully as Rob walked away.

Plockton

I HAVE lovely memories of a holiday we took in September, 1961, when I was twenty-four. We travelled by train from Liverpool, only to arrive in Plockton in the midst of a howling gale.

The stationmaster escorted us to the converted railway carriage which was to be our holiday home and where the kettle was already singing for a welcome "cuppa".

Fortunately, the weather improved and we had a wonderful time.

— *Mrs G.P., Beds.*

J. CAMPBELL KERR.

The fortnight passed quickly. My usual average was two mistakes a day, sometimes more, never fewer. Rob, of course, was entrusted with all the important jobs. Well, I'd discovered that his surname was Greene — ideal for a gardener — so he would be, wouldn't he?

Even so, several times, he happened to be around and helped put some of my worst howlers right, without Steven being any the wiser.

But even when Steven bellowed, "Just look what you've done now!" I didn't care. I thought he looked even more handsome when he was cross.

Finally, it was my last day. If he didn't notice me today . . . He had to notice me! How could he not, when I'd asked for an advance on my pocket money and blown the lot on a pair of expensive pink jeans and matching T-shirt?

"It's your last day, isn't it?" Steven remarked that morning.

He didn't sound quite as heartbroken as I could have wished, so I just said, "Yes," and tried to look soulful.

"So, what can we let you loose on today?" He grinned. "Tell you what, that rock garden behind the lily pond. How do you fancy planting that up with alpines?"

"Oh, great!" I was thrilled. This was the first time he'd actually trusted me to plant anything, so surely it was a good sign?

"I don't think you can actually do much dam —" He caught my eye and stopped mid-sentence.

"The plants are behind the glasshouse and do try to be careful, Albertine. The pond may be full of sludge, but it's still quite deep in places."

"Oh, yes, Steven, I will." Moved by such touching concern for me, I gave him a reassuring — and hopefully dazzling — smile.

BY the end of the morning, I had finished. I'd carefully read all the labels, arranged the plants in matching sizes and contrasting colours and bedded them firmly among the rocks. Surely Steven would be pleased with me this time?

"Hey, Allie, that's looking brill!"

Rob's voice made me swing round and, at the same instant, a large green frog leapt up from under an elephant's ear leaf right alongside me. I gave a shriek, lost my balance and fell headlong into the pool.

As I struggled upright, spluttering, Rob grabbed my hands and hauled me out. As well as being soaked from head to foot, I'd grazed my arm on a sharp rockery stone.

"Ouch." I nursed it tenderly.

"Let me look at that."

Rob was wiping the blood off with his handkerchief when Steven appeared.

"Albertine!" he yelled. "I told you to be careful!"

"It's my fault," Rob put in quickly. "I distracted . . ."

"No, it was my own silly fault." For some reason, I didn't want Rob to get into trouble on my account. I picked at some waterweed on my sodden jeans.

"A frog frightened me and I fell in."

"I knew it! I knew I shouldn't have let you within a mile of that Nymphaea Charles de Meurville."

"That what?"

"That water lily there."

"Oh." For the first time, I saw the huge lily, lying broken and crushed in the churned-up water.

"It's our prize specimen! It cost an arm and a leg and it was just coming into flower for the first time ever."

"Sorry." My mouth turned down at the corners and I sniffed.

"But it'll recover, I'm sure," Rob said. "And it'll bloom all the better next year."

"Yeah, maybe." Steven's face softened. "And worse things happen at sea — or even in lily ponds. Come on, we'd better find you some dry clothes."

With Rob following us, he led me, squelching, to his office at the back of the house. I was just about getting used to the cosy feel of his arm round me when a car came into the yard.

"Oh, good. Here's Louise." Steven waved at the car. "She'll have something you can change into."

I watched as a tall young woman with a shining fall of chestnut hair, dressed in an immaculate cream suit, got out.

"Hi, Lou."

Steven let me go and, to my horror, the two embraced.

"Miss me, darling?" She smiled up at him happily and I distinctly heard my heart, if not break, creak at the seams. I scuffed my filthy trainers in the gravel and Steven turned back to me.

"Lou, darling, Albertine's had a bit of an accident. Can you kit her out with something? Don't want her catching pneumonia, do we?"

"Of course not." Louise held out a manicured hand. "Hello, Albertine. Steven's told me all about you. You poor lamb, let's find you something dry to wear."

She opened the car boot and took out a suitcase and, averting my gaze from Steven and Rob, I trailed after her into the office.

✳   ✳   ✳   ✳

It's summer again as I drive up to Belmont Manor and park in the gravelled yard. As I get out the smart new attaché-case that I bought with part of my prize money, Steven appears.

"Hi, Albertine."

"Hello, Steven."

He hugs me.

"You're looking great."

"So are you. Married life suits you."

I'd heard from Mum that he and Louise were living in a cottage on the estate.

"And how's your little girl? What's she called again?"

"We called her Felicia."

"Let me see." I frown in thought. "Oh, yes. Large tresses of flowers, warm pink buds and tinted with soft apricot, a vigorous climber."

"That's right." He grins. "Blame your mum. She started that fashion in names."

"Well, it could have been worse. I must say, though, I'm actually getting to quite like Albertine at long last."

"It certainly sticks in the mind. When I saw in the gardening mag that the prize for Young Garden Designer of the Year was awarded to Albertine Adams, I knew it was you. So now that we're getting round to revamping that area by the old summerhouse, who else could we call on?"

I smiled reminiscently.

"Well, that's certainly where it all started."

In The Garden

S UMMER in the garden,
The lazy hum of bees,
And brilliant flowers whose petals dance
In every gentle breeze.

The butterflies of varied hue,
Whose beauty brings delight,
Display their lovely, shimmering wings
In summer's golden light.

To tend the summer garden well
Needs patient, tender care,
Sometimes it seems there's little time
To pause and "stand and stare".

But when at last we cease our toil
And take a well-earned rest,
We look with satisfaction at
Our gardens at their best.
— **Rosemary Bennett.**

✳   ✳   ✳   ✳

It had, too. That lunchtime, kitted out in Louisa's genuine designer jeans and sweatshirt, I'd taken my wounded heart off to the tumbledown summerhouse in the furthermost and still totally neglected part of the estate.

As I sat munching my sandwiches and apple, keeping my thoughts well away from Steven, I found myself musing on what could be done with this once lovely area.

If those rampant rhododendrons and camellias sprawling through the overgrown hedges were cut back, it would give them new life — and the view to the distant hills would be opened up. Winding gravel paths could lead the eye to that ruined folly on the horizon, and . . .

Back in the office, my teeth had started chattering and Louise had insisted on draping me in an old corduroy jacket that hung from a hook behind the door. In a pocket was a pencil stub and crumpled old envelope and, my brain racing, I smoothed it out and began to sketch.

"I thought you might still be feeling chilled."

I jumped as Rob appeared. He put a hand on mine and clicked his tongue.

"Yes, you're really cold. Here — I've brought you some of my coffee."

"Thanks, Rob."

I took the vacuum flask top and sipped gratefully. I was hoping he'd go away again so that I could hug my sore heart to myself, but he dropped down beside me on the rickety bench instead.

J. Winkley

"What's this you're doing?"

"Nothing. Just doodling."

I went to shove the envelope back into my pocket but he took it from me.

"It's just some ideas I had for this area of the garden," I said defensively as he frowned over it. "Probably useless."

"No, they look great." He smiled at me and I noticed, really noticed, for the first time what lovely dark blue eyes he'd got. And his eyelashes were even longer than Steven's.

"This path." He pointed to my sketch. "What else could you do with it?"

"I thought I'd put in clumps of silver birches for it to wind through. Then loads of snowdrops. My mum and gran and I went to a garden last February, just to see their snowdrops. There were hundreds of people there. It would bring in loads of money."

"And Eranthis hyemalis." He grinned as I looked blank. "Golden aconites. Wild daffodils later, maybe fritillary. I think the ground is damp enough."

Then he suddenly stopped and looked a bit embarrassed.

"Sorry, I seem to be taking over your design."

"No, it's all right. I was just filling in time in my lunch break."

He looked down at me and I had the feeling that he had a good idea why.

"Come on, Steven will have the hides off both of us if we're late back!"

✳   ✳   ✳   ✳

"Yes, Steven," I repeat now. "This is definitely where it all began."

We both look round as a green van pulls into the courtyard.

"Rob's been planting up that bog garden at the Old Rectory."

"Smart vehicle," Steven says. "And I like the logo — *Greene Fingers*."

"You are coming to the wedding, aren't you?"

"Of course! Lou and I wouldn't miss it for the world. You two will make a superb team, I'm sure."

"Hi, there." Rob comes up to us and they shake hands.

"Right, Steven," I say. "You're our first big commission. Lead the way."

As I told you, I knew I'd never be a gardener. Even now, my soon-to-be husband, when he wants to wind me up, will say, "Make sure you plant those the right way up, won't you?"

And to really wind me up, he adds, "Albertine".

But I didn't say anything about not being a garden designer. After all, as my mum would say, what else could I be with a name like mine? ■

All In A Good Cause

by Annie Harris.

I WAS just replacing the distributor cap when Libby came up behind me.

"Hello, Granny."

"Hello, love." I smiled down at her. "I won't kiss you. I'm really oily."

I wiped my hands on a rag, then put down the yellow bonnet. Libby ran her palm down the car's side.

"Granny, when you're too old to drive Galadriel can I have her?"

I laughed.

"You won't want this old thing by the time you're old enough to drive. You'll want a nice new car of your own."

"No, I won't, honestly. I love her. I was telling Mr Bradley all about her on the way into school this morning. He likes old cars, too. He's got a really old red sports car with googly headlights."

"My goodness, that sounds great. But I don't think I'll swap Galadriel." I patted the gleaming top of my Citroen 2CV. "There we are — as good as new, old lady. I'll put you away later."

"I heard Daddy say to Mummy that you must be dotty, talking to your car. And Mummy said it didn't surprise her in the least, because anyone who talks to their cabbages is going to be dotty enough for anything."

"Oh, dear," I said brightly. "Well, come on in and tell me all about school."

I headed straight for the kitchen sink to wash my hands.

"Get the biscuit tin out, will you, love?"

"Mummy said I mustn't have your biscuits," Libby said mournfully.

"Oh?" I turned my head to look at her.

Illustration by David Young.

"They're full of white sugar and that's poison. I told her you eat them every day and you're all right, but she doesn't listen to me."

She doesn't listen to me, either, I wanted to add, but it's not a grandmother's job to interfere.

"Lucky I made some muesli bars this morning, then — with brown sugar."

"Can I ask you a favour, Granny?"

"Of course, love."

"Well, Mr Bradley wants to raise some more money for that school in Africa where he used to teach."

MY heart sank slightly. I'd already sponsored Libby twice recently — for a car wash, and a six-hour silence. Both in a very worthwhile cause, but even so . . .

"So you want me to sponsor you again? Well, of course I will, but I can't do it for quite so much this time." I pulled a face. "I've just had a speeding ticket."

"Oh, Granny!" Libby stared at me in horror. "Not another one! Daddy said

91

to Mummy last time, when is your mother —"

I didn't want to hear this and interrupted quickly.

"Well, I was only doing thirty-two miles an hour then, and this time thirty-three, but the vultures caught me. So you see, I'm a bit short of cash this week."

"That doesn't matter because it's not to sponsor me anyway."

Well, that was a relief.

"Do you want me to bake some more cakes?"

"No, it's nothing like that." She paused, helping herself to another muesli bar. "You know your special T-shirt — the one you keep wrapped up in tissue paper?"

"My Bilbo Baggins one? Yes, of course."

"Could I borrow it? I'll be very careful with it."

"But it's too big for you, love. When you're older, perhaps I'll give it to you then."

Mind you, it would be a wrench to give it away — even to my beloved granddaughter. I'd bought that T-shirt at a very special Glastonbury Festival. One that had happened so many years ago that it seemed like another lifetime now, and the young me another person altogether.

"No, I don't want to wear it. Mr Bradley was telling us in art class yesterday about an exhibition he's been to, and it was all about T-shirts. Lots of really famous people had signed them and it was all for charity."

I HAD to admit that I was getting a bit tired of our Mr Bradley.

"Oh, yes. I read about that. Sounds like fun."

"Darren said it would be a good idea if we did that as our contribution to the school fête, to raise money for Africa. Mr Bradley wasn't sure at first, but then he said, 'Why not?'

"We don't know any very famous people," she went on earnestly. "But it'll be really good, Granny. We're painting the backgrounds and making cardboard frames, so they'll be like pictures on the wall."

"That sounds great."

"And Mrs Gillespie thinks it's a good idea, too. She says she hasn't got anything suitable, but she's lending one of Mr Gillespie's T-shirts. It's got arrows all over it."

"Arrows?"

"Yes, and it says," she recited carefully, "*Property of Her Majesty's Prison, Dartmoor.*"

Goodness. I would view Mr Gillespie, the husband of Libby's headmistress, with more respect next time I was summoned to his lair at our local bank to discuss my overdraft.

"What about your mum and dad? Are they giving anything?"

"Oh, Mummy and Daddy don't wear T-shirts. Daddy says they're only for teenagers, but you wear them, don't you, Granny?"

"Well —"

"They're going to make a donation, but that's not the same, is it?"

"No, not really."

"Please, Granny. I've got to take in something good!"

"All right, then." I ruffled her hair. After all, I told myself, it was all in a good cause, wasn't it?

*   *   *   *

It was late on the Saturday afternoon when I arrived at the fête, but even so the school carpark was still crowded. As I headed for the entrance, I bumped straight into Libby and my daughter, Alison.

"Hello, love. How are you, my poppet?" I kissed them both.

"Hello, Mum. You're running a bit late."

"Yes, sorry. I was weeding the veg garden and forgot the time. What did you think of the exhibition?"

"All right, I suppose." She wrinkled her nose slightly.

Dear Alison! I smiled fondly at her. She was a wonderful wife, mother and daughter. If only there had been just a few of my genes in her. I suppose there must have been, but there were times when she seemed more like my great-aunt Agatha than either me or her father.

"Come on, Granny." Libby seized my hand. "I'll show you the way."

Alison looked at her watch.

"Bye, Mum. Don't be long, Libby, please."

"All right, Mummy."

Libby led me past the various stalls to the assembly hall. I paid my entrance money, walked in, then gasped.

The walls were lined with cardboard "picture frames", rows of them, large and small. And every frame contained a T-shirt, with its donor's name where the artist's would have been.

COME on, Granny." Libby was tugging me across the room. "I want to show you my picture."

Libby's T-shirt, a tiny pink one with a blue teddy bear, was framed against some very strange-looking bears — at least, I supposed they were bears! — playing ring-o'-roses.

But it was the T-shirt that held my attention. I remembered it so clearly. I'd bought it for her in our local market, but I'd had no idea that Alison, so down to earth and unsentimental, had all these years carefully kept that small reminder of Libby's first summer.

"I painted the bears." Libby was pointing proudly.

"They're really lovely." I blinked away a tear.

"Mr Bradley painted that one in the corner. Oh, here he is."

I turned to see a tall, fair-haired man in T-shirt and jeans walking towards us.

"Mr Bradley, this is my granny. Now I must go — Mummy's waiting for me."

"Bye, lovey."

I kissed her and then straightened up to find the art teacher smiling down at me, his blue eyes twinkling.

"Ah, Libby's famous grandmother — she talks endlessly about you. Hi, I'm Martin Bradley."

He held out a large, tanned hand and I shook it.

"Judy. Judy Green." I looked around me. "What a lot of work all this must have been for you."

"A labour of love, I assure you. Although, to be fair, I made certain the kids did most of the work."

Seaside Joys

*T*HE beauty of the
*seashore
Upon a summer's day,
The shingle and the
golden sand
Where happy children
play.*

*Soft waves are breaking
on the shore,
The cry of gulls above,
The seaweed and the
dainty shells,
Such things all children
love.*

*These simple things once
brought delight
In distant years gone by,
And children still find
happiness
Beneath a summer sky.*
— Rosemary Bennett.

"Good thinking." I went to move away, but then stopped as I suddenly looked at his T-shirt. "Oh, my goodness! How marvellous. That's Middle Earth, and there's Bilbo Baggins's hobbit hole and —" I jabbed a finger at a hard chest "— there's Rivendell."

I suddenly realised what I was doing and drew back.

"Sorry."

L IBBY told me you were a Tolkien fan and I see she was right."

"Oh, I am," I said fervently. "Do you mind my asking where you got it? I've had my Bilbo Baggins T-shirt for so long that it's fading. I'd love to get one like yours."

"Actually, it's a one-off. I designed and printed it myself."

"You did? Well, it's wonderful. I suppose I'd better have a look round."

"I'll show you your exhibit if you like."

He led me across to a large picture frame, painted in soft gold, and there, against a beautiful watercolour background of the folded hills and little fields

of Bilbo's beloved Shire, was my T-shirt.

"What do you think of it?"

"It looks fantastic. Did you do the background?"

"Yes. Libby told me all about your shirt, so I felt it deserved the best. I gather you got it at Glastonbury. At least, I figured that's what Libby meant when she said Glassbury!"

"We went to one of the early festivals." I smiled, but it was more to myself than at him. "It poured the whole time, our tent was flooded out, the mud came over the tops of our wellies and . . ." I stopped, my mind full of those faraway scenes.

"It was absolutely wonderful," he finished for me.

"Yes. Well, it was our honeymoon, you see — Dave and me."

"Is he here?" He looked around the hall.

"No," I said softly. Those carefree, loving days had been so vivid for a moment that I found it hard to return to the present.

"Dave died when Alison was the same age as Libby is now."

"I'm so sorry." His face clouded in real sympathy. "That must have been very tough."

"Well, it's a long time ago." Gently I ran my hand down my T-shirt. "But this is very precious to me."

"Of course. Thank you for lending it to us. We'll take very good care of it, I promise."

"I know you will."

We stood uncertainly for a moment, then I finally managed to pull myself together.

"I'd better have a look round the rest of the exhibits."

"Right. I hope you enjoy the show.'"

Some of the "pictures" were amazing and all of them very artistic. This was a teacher who certainly knew how to get the best out of the children.

I particularly liked Mr Gillespie's offering, set against a beautifully painted backdrop of grim grey tors. And Darren's grandad's displayed a youthful — and gorgeous — Marilyn Monroe reclining against a *HOLLYWOOD* background.

Darren's own contribution was a bright red shirt with black letters proudly proclaiming *My dad knows a lot but my grandad knows everything*, while Mr Bradley's was a Union Jack shirt, surrounded by a collage of evocative scenes of the British countryside.

Just as I was getting to the end, he came over to me.

"What do you think?"

"Brilliant — it's really great. You should be proud of yourself, Mr Bradley."

"Thank you. And it's Martin, by the way. Look, it's nearly over, but they're still serving tea. Can I get you a cup?"

"Thank you, Martin, but only on condition that I pay. Believe me, I'm getting off lightly this time. Libby keeping quiet for six hours last term cost me an arm and a leg!"

HOW'S Galadriel?" he asked over tea at the child-sized chairs and tables.

"Fine ever since I put in new spark plugs, thanks. She was a bit sluggish before that."

He glanced through the canteen window to where the yellow bonnet was just visible.

"She suits you. Talking of Galadriel, have you seen all the films?"

"'Lord Of The Rings'? I've got the first two parts — I thought they were marvellous — but I haven't managed to buy the third one yet."

"Oh, but you must. It's brilliant."

"Well, to be honest, I seem to spend most of my spare cash paying speeding fines these days."

He grinned.

"I see. My nephew gave me the DVD for Christmas. Would you like to borrow it?"

"That's very kind of you, but I've only got an old video player."

"Well, tell you what. How about coming to my place next weekend to watch it? The last battle for Middle Earth is amazing!" He blew out his cheeks. "And I'll rustle up something to eat. I'm told that my lentil and vegetable curry is to die for.'"

It was.

And it was certainly much better than the moussaka I gave him the following week, though of course he was too polite to say so. But he did love my chocolate puddle pudding.

By then, we had watched the whole trilogy twice through, and I knew all about how Martin had gone out to teach in Africa for a year and ended up staying twenty-five. I also heard how he had never somehow got round to marrying, mainly because most young women didn't fancy the idea of living in Africa.

He'd told me about the sunrises over the *veldt* when the whole world hushes and holds its breath, and the sunsets when the sky is scarlet flames. I didn't tell him that Africa had always held a magical attraction for me, that I watched every TV programme I could find on it and for years had had a secret yearning to go there myself. Perhaps I would tell him one day, but not yet . . .

And he told me about the school that he was helping, how he'd raised money for pens and paper, art equipment and text books, and now he wanted to provide help with uniforms and fees, which even at a few pence a day were beyond the reach of many families. He also told me he was going back out there during the next school holiday.

"Do you have any more money-raising projects in the pipeline?" I asked, just as he was leaving.

"Well —" there was that smile again "— it's funny you should ask that."

✳   ✳   ✳   ✳

Which is why today I am standing on the tiny platform of a fire engine's ladder high above the school playground, harnessed by a strong elastic rope. Yes, I'm doing a bungee jump, not over a river, but above a large square of foam mattress.

Almost everyone in our little town seems to be sponsoring the jump, and most of them are here with their tiny faces peering up at me. If I dared to look down I'd probably be able to pick out Libby, there with Robin and Alison, who, after subjecting me to the sternest lecture yet of the just-when-was-I-going-to-grow-up-and-finally-start-acting-my-age variety, had really been very generous with their contribution.

Martin has raised enough money for a new classroom, he told me, but right at this moment I don't care. I just want to be on the ground again. Now. If not sooner.

Talking of Martin, he's here beside me on the platform, strapped into his own harness. I catch his eye and he grins, a grin that is becoming very dear to me.

"All right, Judy?"

I wipe my sweaty hands down my brand-new Middle Earth T-shirt, gulp and nod.

"All right!"

He takes one of my hands in his big, warm one and gives it a quick squeeze. I'm still smiling as we jump happily together into space. ■

WOOLLYBACKS" — that's what the townspeople call us farming folk living here on the edge of the wild moors. But we have a wisdom beyond them, for all their fancy bonnets and costumes.

I can watch the fluttering of a grouse's wings and tell you when snow is coming. I can show you a nightjar's nest lying bare on the moorland. And sometimes, when the wind whispers softly over the fields, I can hear the golden corn growing.

Barney understood our ways right from the start. How my heart rose when I watched him jump down from the cart that summer's day.

It was a June morning, ten years to the day since our beloved Queen Victoria had come to the throne, when Farmer Craven and his wife set off for the hiring fair at Moorsedge.

"The chickens want clearing out, Hannah. And there's straw to spread in the barn for the cattle," he told me as he hitched the horse to the wagon.

I worked hard all day and was just scattering the last bundle of straw when I heard the clatter of wheels and the horse's hooves that announced their return.

Barney was sitting on the back of the cart, his long legs dangling. A well-made man, all of six feet tall, his face had been browned by the sun.

Illustration by Len Thurston.

98

His stockman's crook lay by his side.

As he jumped down from the cart, he caught me peeping out from behind the barn doors. Most of the workmen would have winked or given a friendly call. But he just looked at me with slow, thoughtful eyes.

Farmer Craven nodded my way.

"That's Hannah, Barney. She's a good, strong lass and a hard worker. You'll be seeing her at supper tonight."

I was glad to hear him praise me to a stranger. It wasn't a common occurrence.

Barney didn't open his mouth. He just raised a hand to his hat, respectfully, as if I were a lady, and led the horse into the barn.

I felt awkward that evening, sharing the scrubbed table with the men, and I kept my head well down over the stew Mrs Craven had prepared.

Through the curtain of my hair I could see Barry watching me. When he spoke, his voice was surprisingly quiet for such a powerfully built man.

"Do you live on the farm, Hannah?"

"I sleep in a garret over the stables."

He nodded and I thought he had done with me. But when Mrs Craven put down a plate of home-made bread and half a farmhouse cheese, he pushed it across to me, polite as you please.

Country Ways

by Elizabeth Summerhill.

"Where bides your family?"

It would have sounded curt coming from some others. But Barney was different. He seemed to care.

"Father is the stockman and Mother the housekeeper at a manor house up north."

Farmer Craven's cider made me bold.

"Where do you hail from, Barney?"

"Nowhere special. I travel from farm to farm, taking work where I can find it."

I wanted to ask him more — whether he had a family, if the travelling life was lonely, and especially if he had a girl. But I could see Mrs Craven listening with half an ear.

When he had finished, Barney went into the yard, stripped off his shirt and washed under the pump. He was to sleep in the stable.

That night I lay awake thinking of him down below in that draughty barn. How lucky I was to be warm in my garret. Farmer Craven and his wife had been kind to me, right from the day I had knocked on the farmhouse door seeking work.

WE rose at dawn and Farmer Craven sent me to Five-acre Field to hoe beet. My heart sank. Navvies were building the new railway line down in the valley. I was wary of passing these rough working men.

The sun was a red ball on the horizon when two of them, pickaxes dangling, pushed through the hedge.

"Why, here's a bonnie lass, then!" One circled me appraisingly.

"Fair indeed," put in the other.

I didn't hear the boots tramping across Five-acre, only the voice, quiet and self-controlled.

"Throw your words at me, not the girl."

Barney stood there, powerful hands curled into fists. Moments later the workmen slunk away. I basked in a warm glow. I couldn't remember a time when anyone else had ever stood up for me.

"Thank you, Barney." I bowed my head shyly. "They've teased me before."

"Maybe so, but they'll not do it again, I'm thinking. If they do, you call me."

The next day my back ached with the beet hoeing. I ran a hand over my damp forehead. Barney halted work and passed me a flask of water.

"I'll be taking my snap shortly, by the sheep pen." He didn't ask me outright, but I knew it was an invitation to join him.

We sat in the shade with our food and after a while I asked him something that had been puzzling me.

"Have you always been a casual worker, a wanderer?"

"For two years, thereabouts."

"You've never had a home?"

He plucked a stalk of wheat and rubbed it in his hands.

"A while ago I lived with my brother, Isaac."

There was a sadness in his voice.

"What happened?" I asked.

The words came slowly, as though they'd been tied up inside him too long.

"Isaac and I were navvies, working on the Fore Bank Moss tunnel. One day there was an earthfall. Isaac didn't come home. He was all the family I had."

"Oh, Barney!" I touched my fingers to his forearm.

"I've been a loner ever since, going from farm to farm. Couldn't be much bothered with people — until I met you."

I tried to think of words to comfort him. But his pain was too deep, and words seemed so empty. I squeezed his hand and hoped that he understood.

"Oh, Barney! Would you like to see a nightjar's nest?" I asked hesitantly, trying to brighten his mood.

"I've never seen one." His eyes lit up.

Dusk was falling as I led him along the steeply rising moorland track. There, beneath a bank of bracken, I pointed to the marbled eggs, blotched with ash grey, resting in their nest of leaves.

Barney whispered into the night air.

"They're so delicate, so beautiful, Hannah."

The nightjar called its churring trill — coo-ick . . . coo-ick.

We walked away. His hand found mine and held it.

SUMMER gave way to autumn and I opened my heart to Barney.

"It's been lonely here on the Craven farm. It's so far from my mother and father."

"But you've made friends, haven't you?"

"With navvies and farm labourers? No, Barney. What would I want with them?"

"But I'm a farm worker." He looked teasingly at me.

"You're different, Barney."

"You've brought me back from the darkness, Hannah. Made me see the joy in life again."

His words spun round and round in my head that night.

*　　*　　*　　*

Winter came. The air was sharp and cold on the day we stood by the gleaming rails to watch for the first steam engine.

Farmers, labourers and navvies had gathered from miles around. We jostled into the crowd.

Soon the iron rails began to shiver and in the distance I saw a cloud of smoke. The great engine hurtled towards us, steam belching from its funnel.

Not thinking what I was doing, I threw myself into Barney's arms. They closed round me, safe and warm. The engine thundered by in a shower of sparks and red glowing coals and soon it was only a cloud of steam in the distance, disappearing into the dark tunnel.

I struggled excitedly to set myself free, but Barney would not let me go.

"Barney! Did you ever see the likes of it?"

"I barely noticed, Hannah."

"But the smoke, the fire! How wonderful!"

"They were nothing to me. I noticed only the sweet smell of your hair, the warmth of your skin and the joy of holding you in my arms."

I was so happy as he lowered his lips to mine.

SNOW came late, as winter merged into spring. The sky was a stormy ochre, heavy with swirling black clouds. A nasty blizzard whitened the hills. On top of it all, Farmer Craven fell ill.

I was spreading extra straw in the barn for the cattle when Barney burst in, tying a hank of rope round his loose smock, his hat pulled low over his forehead.

"The lambs will be buried. I'll have to dig them out."

"In this? You can't, Barney. There'll be drifting."

"I can't let them perish."

"Then I'm coming with you." One look at my set face and he knew no words would stop me. He threw a cloak around my shoulders and on top we each wore a couple of thick hessian sacks tacked together. We took shovels and trudged out into the frozen yard.

Once on the open moor the wind cruelly whipped at our faces. We fought on through deepening drifts. The sheep pen was no more than a smear of grey stones looming out of the snow.

"They'll be in the lee of the drystone wall," Barney shouted. Hour after hour we dug to free the trembling lambs. We wiped them down and covered them in dry, sweet-smelling straw stacked in the roofed pen.

Our limbs were heavy, our frozen bodies exhausted by the time we finished.

We staggered back to the farmhouse through the deep snow, Barney's lantern throwing shadows around us.

Mrs Craven had the fire blazing, a pot of thick vegetable broth on the stove and hot toddies to hand. She fussed over us like a clucking hen. We huddled in to the fire and sipped the fortifying drink.

Farmer Craven came in then, still pale from the fever. He took our hands.

"You've saved my livelihood, working out there in that storm tonight. I won't forget what you've done."

"You're family now, you and Barney, Hannah," Mrs Craven added.

The following Saturday we each found a gold sovereign in our wages.

Cley Mill, North Norfolk

*W*HAT *wonderful memories I have of my native Norfolk!
Cley Mill is a lovely old building and now makes excellent holiday
accommodation.*

*I recall climbing to the top and standing out on the deck where the
views are superb — right across the marshes and countryside.*

*Two of my ancestors were fishermen here, way back in the 1600s,
and visiting this mill made me nostalgic for my Norfolk childhood and
the beauty of the coast in all its moods.*

— Mr J.C., Gloucs.

J. CAMPBELL KERR.

As the days lengthened, cherry trees blossomed in the orchard and skylarks wheeled high in a deep blue sky.

Barney and I were broadcasting corn in Five-acre when he changed my world for ever. We reached the end of a row just as the ground trembled with the coming of an engine. Barney took me in his arms.

"The first time this train came by I let you go, Hannah. But not this time.

"I'm going to hold you close this year and every year God gives us, if you'll let me."

I raised my voice against the roar of the engine and the hiss of steam.

"Yes! Oh, yes!"

That night we told Farmer Craven. Mrs Craven smiled.

"I've been waiting for this. I knew it wouldn't be long."

Farmer Craven, now fully recovered, took the clay pipe from his mouth and looked at us proudly.

"That day when you dug out my sheep, I told you I wouldn't forget. And I haven't.

"I'm making over the empty cowman's cottage and thirty acres to you both, for a peppercorn rent and a fair share of vegetables from the kitchen garden."

Mrs Craven's apple-red cheeks glowed.

"We haven't been blessed with children, Zachary and me, but the good Lord has brought you two our way instead."

I was so overwhelmed that I threw myself into her arms.

"There, there, girl. Anyone would think I was your mother."

"As good as, Mrs Craven. As good as." I burst into tears. Then I leaned over and kissed Mr Craven's rough, stubbly cheek. His voice was gruff with embarrassment.

"That's a more generous offer than any man could hope for, sir." Barney crushed the old man's hand in his and, lifting Mrs Craven's hand to his mouth, planted a gentle kiss.

*　　*　　*　　*

Barney has sheared off the last fleece now and the sheep are gambolling in the warm sunshine. I can scarcely believe that a year has flown by since Parson Trimbley married us, and I count my blessings every day.

Soon there will be three of us. Mrs Craven has done nothing but fuss since she discovered.

"A baby!" she cried. "I knew there'd be a baby!"

We're lucky, Barney and I, to have found each other.

After supper we will walk up on to the hill to look for the nightjar's nest. A pair have been courting for days; we've heard their trilling echo across the darkening moorland at nightfall.

It's a special place for us. For it was there that Barney first held my hand and our destinies became one. ■

A Growing Family

Illustration by Mark Viney.

by Rachel McCourt.

J ANEY set the steaming casserole dish down on the table.

"Dinner," she announced, waiting expectantly.

Her husband, Mark, and Dylan, her son, were deep in conversation about football. Mark disengaged himself first and looked up at her. Dylan's gaze followed.

"What is it?" her son asked.

"Shepherd's pie," Janey said.

"Brilliant!" Dylan lost little time in tucking into his plateful.

105

She watched the two boys in her life devouring their food.

"Not hungry?" Mark asked, looking at his wife, who was pushing her meal round the plate with her fork.

Janey smiled and excused herself from the table.

"Won't be a moment," she said, as lightly as she could.

She stood with her back against the bathroom door and waited for the nausea to subside. When it did, she drank some water from the tap and took a deep breath before returning to the kitchen.

As she began to eat she realised how hungry she was, and barely said a word until her plate was clean. The boys had chatted throughout the meal and now they sat back, relaxed, passing amiable comments.

She regarded them with a smile. You'd never know, she thought, that they weren't biological father and son. They got on so well together.

She thought back to those anxious days before she and Mark got married. How worried she had been that Dylan would never cope with a new father.

She remembered the little exchange she and Dylan had used to share.

"Two's company," he would say.

"Three's a crowd," she'd reply.

They hadn't needed anyone else. But then Mark came along, and despite Janey's anxieties, he and Dylan had got along famously. Three was no longer a crowd — it was a family.

But, Janey wondered, if three was a family, what was four?

S TILL feeling queasy?"

Mark's gentle hands rested on her shoulders. He leaned forward to kiss her cheek.

"Not so bad at the moment," she told him. "It comes and goes."

"I hope it's a girl," he said, slipping his hands down to caress her stomach. It was still flat, though Janey felt bloated.

"No, I hope it's a boy. Oh, I don't know — I'm just so excited. Maybe it'll be one of each!"

"Hah! Funny," she said contentedly.

Instantly, her mood switched. She found this happened a lot at the moment — one minute she was dreamily happy, the next she was on the verge of tears.

"How will Dylan cope when I'm in hospital?" She twisted round to face Mark.

"He'll be fine," Mark said, "and you won't be kept in for long."

"But what if I am?" She pulled away fretfully. "I've never left him before, not even for a night. We've not even had our honeymoon yet!"

"What's a honeymoon?" Dylan's voice preceded his eager footsteps down the stairs.

"I thought you were getting ready for bed," Janey said.

"Done," he said. "What's a honeymoon?"

"Well, it's a kind of holiday people have when they get married," Mark explained.

"Why's it called a honeymoon?" Dylan plonked himself down on the sofa. "Is it because you moon over your honey?" He pulled a serenely grinning face over clasped hands.

Janey and Mark both laughed.

"Something like that," she said.

"But you two do that all the time," Dylan said, rolling his eyes, "so you must be on a honeymoon all the time."

"You, young man," Mark said, sitting down next to Dylan and tickling him mercilessly until he howled with laughter, "should be in bed."

✳   ✳   ✳   ✳

After school the following day, Janey noticed that Dylan was much quieter than usual.

"You all right, sweetheart?" she asked, as they walked along the road.

Dylan nodded, but Janey noticed his downcast eyes and the uncharacteristic silence.

"What's up?"

"Nothing." He kicked a stone out of his way.

Janey squeezed his hand but stayed quiet.

"Craig Richards has got a baby brother," Dylan said suddenly.

"Oh, yes?" Janey said lightly.

"Yes." Dylan fell silent again.

Janey looked up through the trees at the blue sky above. What was she to do? Dylan was going to hate having a new baby. It wouldn't be long before he thought about the fact that Mark was the baby's father and not his. He'd feel ostracised, different, pushed out of the family.

Three's a family — four's a crowd!

They walked the rest of the way in silence.

"I made you a chocolate cake," she said, once they were home.

Dylan's eyes lit up and he fell on the cake like he hadn't been fed in days. Janey noticed, though, that he'd only taken a few mouthfuls before he slowed down and started poking his finger in the icing.

"Will I have a baby brother?" he asked, prodding the cake fiercely.

Janey felt her heart fluttering. She wished so much that Mark was here to help her. What was she supposed to say? She sensed that taste in her mouth which heralded an attack of nausea.

"Well," she said eventually. "I don't know about that."

Dylan mashed his cake.

"Would you like it if you did?" she asked, trying to keep her voice as neutral as possible. It sounded unnaturally high to her own ears.

Dylan looked up at her, gazing into her eyes for a moment, with just the same look he'd had as a new-born baby, knowing yet curious at the same time. He began to chew his lip — a habit she knew he copied from her.

"Dunno," he replied at last. "Can I watch TV?"

"Of course you can," Janey said, following him into the living-room, unsure whether to feel disappointed or relieved.

W ELL, at least he hasn't asked where babies come from," Mark said later. "I'm not sure we're ready for that conversation yet."

Janey smiled, but her eyes remained anxious.

"From what I can gather," she said, "most children find it hard when a new sibling comes along, but it's going to be harder for Dylan, and I don't know what to do."

Herbal

Ginger

G INGER — or *zingiber officinale*, as it is officially known — has been cultivated for so long that no-one knows exactly where it originated. Used first of all in China and India, it reached the west at least two thousand years ago.

Ginger flowers have an aromatic smell, but it is the root of the plant that is most commonly used. Pulverised fresh ginger applied as a poultice two to three times a day was supposed to be a cure for baldness in China many years ago, but there is, unfortunately, no modern scientific research to back up this claim.

"How will it be harder for Dylan?" Mark asked.

"Well, you know, you not being his real dad and all that — he might think that the new baby is more a part of the family than he is."

"Oh, that," Mark said, his brow lowering. He looked away. "I always forget about that," he said, "until you bring it up again."

Janey wasn't sure how much of this was meant as a rebuke, but she was in the mood for an argument.

"Look," she said with a sigh. "Dylan is my son —"

"He's mine, too!"

"Yes," she continued. "But you know what I mean."

"Well, you certainly seem to remind me as often as you can," Mark said. "I know exactly what you mean."

Another time, Janey thought, with fewer hormones flooding her tired body, she'd have risen to the comment. Now, though, it was like a warm sea lapping at her feet on a balmy night. Her feel-good hormones had kicked in again, which was probably just as well.

"Mark," she started softly.

He scraped his fingers through his hair and looked sheepish.

"I'm sorry," he said, moving over to give her a cuddle. "I don't know what I'm thinking of. Blame the hormones!"

"You're not the one with the raging hormones!" Janey laughed.

"What do they call it?" he said. "Sympathetic pregnancy? Anyway, I think

108

Know-how!

There have, however, been studies that suggest ginger can help treat arthritis, as it is anti-inflammatory and pain-relieving. Traditionally it has also been used to treat motion sickness, morning sickness and other forms of nausea.

There must be something about ginger that works because, incredible as it may sound, it is used in half of all Chinese herbal prescriptions!

we just have to talk to Dylan about this properly. There's no point trying to guess what he's thinking."

"I know," Janey replied, but she looked away. She was saddened to think that after the blissful time they'd all shared, the honeymoon was over.

✳   ✳   ✳   ✳

Janey collected Dylan from school the next day. He came charging out of the classroom, gave his mum a quick cuddle and then careered down the field after his friend, Craig.

"Dylan," she started, once she had caught up with him, and they were walking hand in hand.

"Yes, Mum?" he said, looking up at her.

"Does Craig like having a baby in his family?"

Dylan glanced at her with a curiously adult look.

"Dunno," he said. "S'pose."

Janey felt at a loss for what to say next. They walked a little further in silence.

"Mummy," Dylan said. "Do you want a baby?"

Janey felt herself flush hot then drain cold, leaving her skin feeling prickly.

"Well," she said guardedly. "I think it might be nice if we all wanted one, yes."

Dylan nodded, but said nothing. Janey tried to figure out what he was thinking, but his face was giving nothing away.

When they arrived home Janey sank down on to a kitchen chair.

"Dylan, I need to talk to you," she said.

"What's up, Mum?" he asked, slinging an arm round her shoulders.

"You know I love you, don't you? And that Mark loves you very much as well?"

"Yes," Dylan replied slowly, clearly aware that some important information was about to follow.

"It doesn't mean that we love you any the less whatsoever, but families change and grow. It just means that there's even more love to go around . . ."

"Mum, what are you talking about?"

Janey took a deep breath.

"We're going to have a baby," she blurted out.

Dylan's eyes grew wide as he stared at her. Suddenly he shot his little fist into the air in a triumphant gesture and whooped loudly.

"Yes!" he cried and threw both his arms round Janey's neck. "At last — I thought it would never happen.

"Can I have a brother?" he went on excitedly. "Then we can play all the time. No, no, I want a sister, then she won't take all my toys. I know," he said decisively. "We can have one of each!"

Janey laughed out loud and hugged her son tightly.

"So, you're happy about this?" she asked.

"It's so cool," he said. "Wait till I tell Craig."

"I was worried you might be upset."

"Why?"

"Oh, you know — two's company, three's a family, all that."

"Yeah, three's a family," he said. "But four's, well, four's a honeymoon, isn't it?"

They both turned their heads as they heard the front door open.

"Mark, Mark!" Dylan called, rushing into the hall. "We're going to have a honeymoon."

Mark laughed as he hugged Dylan and looked enquiringly at Janey. She nodded at him and grinned broadly.

"That's what four makes, apparently," she said. "One big, happy honeymoon!"

*   *   *   *

"So, all's well," Mark said later that evening, when Dylan had gone happily up to bed.

"Yup," Janey replied, but she shook her head. "You know, I really should give Dylan more credit."

"You don't say," Mark said.

"No, I'm serious. All this time I was worried that he hated the idea of a new baby in the family, and all the time he was worried about hurting my feelings because he wanted one."

"He's one in a million, that's for sure."

"Oh, Mark." Janey turned to him suddenly, her face full of panic. "What if I don't love this baby as much as I love Dylan? How can I love two at the same time?"

Mark laughed softly and stroked her hair.

"You worry far too much," he said. "People have been doing this for millennia — it'll be all right."

"I suppose so, but —"

Mark silenced her with a gentle kiss.

"I love you," he said. "And Dylan loves you. And soon there'll be another little person who loves you."

Janey nestled against him and smiled happily. She felt a familiar gnawing feeling in her stomach.

"I need brussels sprouts," she announced suddenly. "Lots of them."

Mark kissed her again.

"I'll see what I can do," he said. ∎

Autumn Alley

AS I walk down
the autumn alley,
My lengthening
shadow behind,
A dapple of dancing
colours
Finds an echo inside
my mind.
A dapple of gold and
crimson,
A dapple of light and
shade,
As I walk down the
autumn alley
Where rollicking
children played.

They played in the
autumn alley,
Kicked bright-hued
leaves about,
Piled them high,
took armfuls and
tossed them
With a gleeful shriek
and shout,
They did not think of
coming winter,
And did not feel the
nip in the air,
And they played in
the autumn alley,
So young and free
from care.

Now I walk down the
autumn alley,
And the sunlight still
is warm,
Still shines on the
trees and gilds them,
A corona round
their form,
And I still hear the
children's voices,
I still hear their shouts
at play,
As I walk down the
autumn alley
On a gentle autumn
day.
— **Deborah Mercer.**

Willie Shand.

A Lifetime

by Marie West.

SHE'D started clearing out the cupboard in the spare bedroom, but hadn't made much progress. She kept coming across little things from the past, which she'd almost forgotten.

Jenny supposed she'd always been something of a hoarder. The clutter had driven her mam to distraction at times. There had been her collection of shells, which you could hold to your ear and hear the sea coming in, along with the coloured pebbles which were scattered about the room. Then there was her store of confetti, which she'd gathered from outside St Barnabas Church after weddings.

She still had some of these mementoes, even after all these years, along with her collection of buttons, and her french knitting, which had never seemed to grow any longer, no matter how hard she tugged at it.

"You've no patience," her mam used to say, but she had really.

When there was something, or someone, worth waiting for, then she had all the patience in the world.

*   *   *   *

When she was six years old, Jenny had decided she'd be a nurse when she grew up, but she didn't have anyone to try out her bandaging on.

At first, she'd practised on Betsy, the rag doll her mam had made for her, and on the old teddy she'd had since she was a baby, but that didn't seem satisfactory. So she'd turned to Tigger, their stripey cat, who'd stood in a frozen attitude while she'd carefully wound the strips of cloth round him, before escaping with one contemptuous bound, scattering his makeshift dressings as he went.

Of Memories

Her mam had agreed that a nurse was a good thing to be, but had said that cats didn't like to be treated like patients, and anyway, Tigger was becoming too old to want to play. So Jenny had reluctantly put away her bandages.

Then she'd heard the lorry pulling in to their street and had gone out to investigate.

THE Hennesseys lived in the three streets of back-to-backs which stood in the shadow of the rope works. The streets were known locally as the Alleys. Ada Hennessey, who had been a Smurthwaite before she was married and could hold her own with anyone, had decided that the Alleys were getting a bad name because of some of the new people who were moving in there.

It was time to move out.

The Smurthwaites, Ada would be the first to admit, had never had two ha'pennies to rub together, but they'd always been decent folk, and respectable.

So Ada had kept her eyes open and found them a house in Adelaide Street. Although it was as poor and cramped as the one where they were living, the people kept their windows clean and their fronts properly step-stoned.

There was even the occasional aspidistra, flaunting

Illustration by Mark Viney.

113

its leaves behind a more affluent window. It looked like a decent place to bring up her family.

Charlie Hennessey, who thought such things were the province of his wife, and who, in any case, liked a quiet life, had gone along with this plan with his customary good humour.

They'd moved in to Adelaide Street at the start of the summer. Neighbours had watched discreetly as the coal lorry had unloaded their possessions, and the four Hennessey children had charged about, making, as old Mrs Walters had said, enough noise to wake the dead. After all, this was a respectable street.

Jenny had gone out to watch, hoping that there would be a girl of her age to play with, but Ruby Hennessey was ten, and her sister May even older. The two boys, who were younger, pulled faces at you when their mam and dad weren't looking, which wasn't very nice.

Jenny had gone in to tell her mam about it, but Sharon Coverdale had told her not to tell tales and to give the family a chance to settle in. But Jenny didn't think that she'd ever want to play with the Hennesseys, who all seemed to be noisy and bossy and looked at you as if they wanted to fight you. And Mrs Hennessey was a bit scary, because she seemed to tell people off a lot.

Yet mysteriously, in a short time, Ada Hennessey had become Aunt Ada, and Jenny was spending most of her time with Jake and his older brother Samuel, who would sometimes consent to join them.

✳   ✳   ✳   ✳

They seemed an unlikely pair to be such good friends. Ada Hennessey, who was a good twelve years older than Sharon, was rough and ready and inclined to speak her mind, while Sharon Coverdale, polite and quietly spoken, had always been the type to keep herself to herself.

It had been when Sharon was doing the weekly wash and had slipped in the wet yard, knocking over the dolly tub in the process, that Ada, hearing the commotion, had come in to investigate and found Sharon lying in the yard. Her hip, which she had banged as she fell, was hurting badly. Ada had taken charge; something which Sharon was to realise came as second nature to her.

"Nothing broken," she'd announced with grim satisfaction, "but you'll be black and blue in the morning."

It hadn't been encouraging, but then Ada had helped her inside and made her as comfortable as possible, before going on to tackle Sharon's abandoned wash. Then she'd joined her in a welcome pot of tea, brushing away Sharon's thanks. It was what neighbours were for, to help out in time of trouble.

It had been the start of a friendship which was to last throughout their lives, and which was to be cemented in a way that neither of them could have envisaged at the time.

As they'd come to know one another better, Sharon had realised that Ada's blunt and outspoken ways couldn't hide her kindness and willingness to offer help where it was needed, so that even Mrs Walters had given her grudging approval. And Ada, who'd thought that Sharon was the sort of fragile person a puff of wind could blow over, had been impressed by the way she'd gone off uncomplaining to her cleaning jobs the next day, even though she must have been in a lot of pain.

As Sharon had said, she was a widow, and she and Jenny relied on the money she earned. Ada could understand that. Even with Charlie working, she had difficulty managing, with six mouths to feed on his modest wages, and on occasion had needed to resort to Mr Parsons, who kept the corner shop.

He would ignore his own uncompromising *No Tick* notice, and help out with a few groceries until pay day, when he knew someone could be trusted.

Still, there was no shame in that. They were all in the same boat round here and helped each other out when they could.

IT was the start of the summer holidays. A crowd of the Adelaide Street children were spending the day on the sands, with the older Hennesseys in charge. They'd decided to go on the penny ferry and be rowed across the bay, which was one of Jenny's favourite things. Afterwards, they'd headed back home along the docks road.

Jenny was walking along with Jake Hennessey, but he'd wanted to keep stopping to look at the boats, so they'd fallen behind. The others had disappeared from sight, despite their shouts of protest.

That was when Jake had become frustrated and angry and had threatened to climb down into one of the boats that were moored nearby and go home across the bay that way.

At seven, Jenny was unmoved by his threats.

"You can't. You're not old enough to row a boat and anyway, it's stealing, so you'd probably have to go to prison for about twenty years."

That had annoyed him even more. Just because she was four months older than him, and a milk monitor, she thought that she knew everything and could boss him about.

"Prison," he'd scoffed, moving jauntily towards one of the fishing cobles to show her he wasn't worried.

He thought that you had to be about ten before you could go to prison, and he was still only six. Besides, he hadn't really meant to steal the boat, so what was she on about?

On the other hand, he wasn't altogether sure if she might be right, so he'd abandoned his plan. They'd trudged home, squabbling half-heartedly because they were tired and hot, only to be met by the older Hennesseys, who were in trouble for leaving them, and had been sent back out to find them.

On the way, Jake had told her about his uncle Danny, who was a sailor, as he intended to be, and then he'd decided to pretend he was rowing a boat all the way home, which had made them both laugh so much that Aunt Ada had said there'd be tears before bedtime.

But there weren't, because that was the day that Jenny decided that she liked Jake Hennessey, and she wouldn't mind having him as a brother, since she didn't have one already.

THEY'D been daring one another to jump off the promenade. It wasn't really all that far down, but she'd landed awkwardly, hurting her foot, which had swollen so much that she could hardly walk.

So Jenny had to lean on Jake as they made their way home, worrying what their mothers were going to say, and blaming each other for wanting to do parachute jumps in the first place.

But it had turned out all right, because that was the day Jake's uncle Danny had come home to stay with them, while he was waiting for another ship. He'd carried Jenny on his back, all the way to the hospital, where she'd had her foot strapped up.

And while Ada had been inclined to blame Jake as the ringleader, Sharon had said they were both as bad as each other, getting up to all kinds of daft pranks.

So no-one got the blame, and Jake had done that trick of opening his eyes very wide, which always made Jenny laugh, and suddenly everything was all right.

Afterwards, Jake had stayed for his tea, and they'd listened to Dick Barton, special agent, which could keep even Jake quiet, and Tigger had sat on her knee when he had realised that she wasn't going to move around and disturb him.

Then they'd played some games of "I spy with my little eye", and snakes and ladders. So it had ended up as a good day, even though her foot was hurting and Jake had accused her of cheating because he'd kept having to go down the snakes.

Still, they'd made friends again before he went home and he'd said he was sorry about her foot. So she quite liked him again, even though he was a bad loser. And then he'd returned, to give her one of his best marbles, the one with all the blue bits inside.

"It's only until you feel better," he'd said sternly as he was leaving. "It's my lucky alley."

And she thought that it must be lucky for everyone. Because after he'd gone, her foot didn't seem to be hurting so much.

✳   ✳   ✳   ✳

Ada had practically brought up her younger brother, Danny, since he'd been a baby. When he'd decided that he wanted to join the Merchant Navy, there had been no holding him back.

116

Enniskillen Castle,
Co. Fermanagh

MY mother's parents belonged to Northern Ireland and during the war years she took me and my younger sisters to stay with them, while my father was away.

I recall the charm and security of the countryside and my large band of Irish cousins. On a Sunday morning we would compete with each other, to see who could find the greatest number of coins dropped by cheery men winding their way home late on a Saturday night.

I got pretty good at it!

— *Mrs M.Y., Glasgow.*

J. CAMPBELL KERR

He'd always been a one for the girls, but had never wanted to settle down, yet Ada, despite her brother's infrequent visits home, still knew him well enough to know that the first time he'd set eyes on Sharon, he was smitten. He'd known she was the one for him.

And Sharon, for her part, was taken by the kindness which lay behind his teasing ways. She knew that he'd have to leave soon, but one day, he told her, when he'd saved enough money, he'd be home for good, and ready to settle down.

For Sharon, it had been the year that she'd taken a searching look at the picture of the young man she'd married, and lost so soon afterwards, and felt that he wouldn't want her to grieve for ever. She would always remember him with that overwhelming love she'd felt for him, but he was gone, and now it was time to move on.

THE year that Jenny was ten had been the year when Tigger had settled himself comfortably in his favourite shady spot in the back yard and had drifted into his final sleep. Jenny had been inconsolable.

Jake, unnerved by the magnitude of her grief, had brought her their own cat, Flossie, who had stood bewildered and affronted in the strange environment she'd suddenly found herself in, until being rescued by an irate Ada, who'd told Jake that you couldn't just replace Jenny's cat like that. Even Jenny hadn't been grateful.

"It won't be Tigger," she'd hiccupped through her tears. "It's not the same."

They'd got another cat eventually, a black cat called Sooty, and Jenny had loved Sooty, but she knew that she didn't love him in the same way as Tigger.

She didn't really understand why, because Sooty was much nicer and liked to play and would snuggle up on her knee when he wanted to sleep, even if she was reading a comic and disturbing him.

Then her mam had told her that you could love different people in different ways, and Jenny had thought she was going to say more, but she hadn't.

The next year, Jake's uncle Danny had come back to stay for good.

✳　✳　✳　✳

They'd been brambling and had come home with their hands stained purple. At thirteen, Jake thought he was too old to be seen around with a girl. But Jenny didn't really count as a girl, she was someone he'd known practically all his life. Anyway, she was a sort of cousin, now that her mam was married to his uncle Danny.

So when they'd handed their brambles over, to be made into pies, they'd gone down to the sands — and that was when they'd bumped into that awful Edward Thomas. He was always hanging around, and Jenny seemed to like him, even though he thought he was better than anyone else, just because his dad owned the butcher's shop.

Jake had that cold feeling that he was being left behind. So he'd gone home and left them to it, kicking a pebble moodily, until a man had told him to stop behaving like a young hooligan.

✳   ✳   ✳   ✳

"We don't see much of Jake these days."

It was Sharon who missed having Jake around. He was a good lad, in spite of his bravado, and many a time she'd struggled to keep a straight face at some of his more outlandish ideas. Still, he was older now, and was turning out to be a real charmer.

Jenny, who had watched helplessly as Jake seemed to be slipping away from her, had simply replied that they'd outgrown one another.

Sharon, about to say something, was stopped by Danny shaking his head slightly. He knew that it was Jake's pride which was keeping him away — he couldn't stand the thought of watching Jenny being monopolised by the Thomas lad.

Maybe the pair of them would learn some sense one day.

✳   ✳   ✳   ✳

Jake had realised his dream when he followed his uncle into the Merchant Navy. It was the life he'd always wanted, but now, after all these years, it was time to go home.

He'd be saying a reluctant farewell to a life at sea, although in moments of complete honesty, Jake sometimes felt that the call of home was stronger than that of the sea. He missed his family, and there was someone else he missed more.

It might be too late to put things right, but he was going to try.

JENNY was making a terrible mistake. It had dawned on her gradually. When Edward had wanted them to become engaged, it had seemed the right thing to do. They'd always got on well together and his family liked her, so they'd just seemed to drift into a more settled relationship. And getting engaged seemed like the next step.

He had wanted her to have a sapphire and diamond ring, which was beautiful, but which for some reason she knew she couldn't wear, so they'd chosen something else.

It had been when Edward wanted them to decide on a date for their wedding that Jenny had known she couldn't go through with it. She did care for Edward, who was loving and kind and would see to it that she never wanted for anything, but it wasn't enough.

"Are you sure about this? Everyone has last-minute doubts," Sharon said, even though she'd had none herself.

She was finding it difficult to know what else to say. She'd always felt in her heart of hearts that Edward wasn't right for her daughter, but she wanted to be fair to the poor lad. He was a decent enough chap, after all.

The really awful part had been telling Edward, who hadn't done anything to deserve this. They'd had their future all planned out together, but when it came to actual wedding plans, she'd known that she couldn't spend the rest of her life with him.

"Why?" he'd asked, but she hadn't been able to give him a satisfactory answer.

It just didn't feel right; it felt as though something was missing. Like the time when Tigger had died and her mam had brought Sooty home one day. She'd loved Sooty, but he wasn't Tigger.

And that's how she felt now. Because, as she'd been talking to Edward, she'd realised why she couldn't marry him, and realised also that she'd known all along. Edward deserved better than this. Her heart would always be somewhere else, with someone else, and one day he'd return.

And Jenny would be waiting.

SO much had been left unsaid, and this new, grown-up Jake unnerved her. He'd suggested a walk by the sea wall, where they'd walked so many times before, and then it had been easier.

"Do you remember when the old ferry went from here?" he asked, as they walked past.

She smiled, remembering the day he'd threatened to steal the fishing coble, the day she'd thought it might be nice to have Jake as a brother.

"Yes. Everything's changed now," she replied.

"Not everything," he said. "Some things stay the same."

He turned to her.

"What happened? That business with you and Edward Thomas."

Jenny realised that she didn't feel guilty any longer, because Edward had found someone else, and they seemed to be happy together. So she told him the truth.

"When it came to it, it just didn't feel right. Maybe he simply wasn't the one for me." She hesitated, trying to find the appropriate words, but there was only one way she could explain how she'd felt. And she didn't know if now was the time.

"What about you?" she asked.

"I never found the right one," he replied. "At least . . ." He paused, suddenly unsure of himself. And they walked on.

Out of the blue, she remembered something.

"I never gave you your lucky alley back. I still have it at home."

Jake hesitated again, but they'd wasted too much time already. He took a deep breath.

"You could always marry me. Then we could share it."

It wasn't the most romantic proposal in the world, as she told him later, but then, it was Jake's way of declaring his feelings, the same Jake who had infuriated her and made her laugh helplessly when they were children, and who had always been by her side.

"That sounds fair," she answered calmly, while her heart was beating so fast she could hardly contain her happiness. She'd waited so long for this moment.

"Is that a yes, then?" he asked, the old, teasing Jake, who'd always tended to hide his deep emotions behind a gruff kindness.

"Yes," she replied simply, because no more words were needed.

And mysteriously, when they arrived back home, both their families were there, ready to congratulate them, as though they'd known what would happen.

But if they both noticed the satisfied glance which passed between Sharon and Ada, they made no comment. After all, like themselves, they'd waited a long time and were happy for them.

✳ ✳ ✳ ✳

When Jake had come to look for her, Jenny had been replacing all the clutter back in the cupboard. After all, there was nothing there that could be thrown away. It was a cupboard full of memories, and it would stay that way. Memories, happy and sad, were too precious to lose. Like the memories of all the years they'd spent together and the times their son, David, and their grandchildren had been born.

There had been the sad memories as well. She thought of her mam and Aunt Ada, both gone now, and the way they had faced up to whatever life had thrown at them, leaving behind the legacy of their caring.

She brushed away the tears which the memories had brought to her eyes. Jake had always been distressed when she was upset, she thought, remembering the time when Tigger had died.

She smiled at him, instead.

"Look what I've found," she said.

It was a blue marble, Jake's lucky alley, which she'd found in the depths of the cupboard.

"Maybe we should pass that on to David," he suggested. "A family heirloom, to pass on to his children."

And he widened his eyes, in the way that he had, and their laughter had wiped away her tears at some of the sad memories.

Then together they carefully replaced safely all those bits and pieces which had measured out their lives.

"Any regrets?" he asked.

"No," she replied without hesitation. "No regrets at all." ■

A Touch Of Romance

BE careful what you call your child, because it can make a huge difference to them. If you have a nice traditional name like Elizabeth, you can hardly go wrong. But if you are called something like, say, Hepzibah, it can be a problem. Not only do you spend your life spelling it, but you also have to contend with the sympathetic glances, if not total disbelief, of friends and officials.

My name is Val. People assume it's short for Valerie, and I let them think that, but they're wrong. I was born on February the fourteenth, and my father, sentimental soul that he is, thought that Valentine suited me perfectly, even if it is, technically speaking, a man's name.

"Jones is such a dull surname," he had apparently said to my mother. "We must have something interesting to go with it. Something different for our little girl."

I suspect she was too exhausted to protest, and had no better alternative lined up, so Valentine Jones I became, and stayed that way till I was twenty-six.

122

by Joyce Begg.

I met Brian when I was in the DIY store, buying floor tiles for the bathroom of my small but perfectly formed flat.

"They're just in," the young man behind the cash desk said, admiring my choice. "Very handsome. And I believe they're very easy to handle."

His name tag said *Brian, Assistant Manager*, and his smile told me that he was good at friendly professionalism. I automatically smiled back, and handed him my plastic card, hoping there was enough in my account to cover the purchase. He looked at it, then whizzed it through the machine.

That was the extent of our conversation, but I found as I left the store that I was smiling, and enjoying something of a warm glow. I also dreamed of Brian that night, which was insane.

Nice, though.

It was some time before I saw him again. I resisted the urge to return to the store, telling myself I was building far too much on such a fleeting meeting. My reticence was rewarded when I met him accidentally, in the supermarket. Our hands met over the frozen peas.

"Sorry," we said at exactly the same moment, retracting our hands in unison. Then he smiled, and my memory clicked in. He didn't have on his uniform, and there was no name tag, but I recognised the man I had dreamed about.

"It's Valentine, isn't it?" he said, which shocked me into silence. After all, *I* hadn't been wearing a name tag.

"I shouldn't have said that," he went on, "but I remembered your name from your bank card. Valentine Jones. Classy and pretty at the same time."

123

Illustration by William Webb.

I blushed.

"How kind."

He looked around him.

"Look, I don't know how much time you've got, but I'm ready for a coffee, and there's a really nice coffee shop in here. Would you like to join me? After your shopping, of course."

SO that is what we did. He treated me to a cappuccino, and threw in a chocolate chip cookie, which I thought extremely generous for a complete stranger. Not that we remained strangers for long.

"Well, you know that I'm Valentine Jones." I smiled. "But I don't know your name. Apart from Brian, of course."

He hesitated for a fraction of a second.

"Davidson. Brian Davidson."

I held out my hand.

"Nice to meet you, and thank you for the cookie."

So that was the start of our friendship, which in a matter of days became a full-blown romance.

Genuine bolt-of-lightning stuff. We became so completely absorbed in each other that we seemed to see no-one else. I didn't invite him to meet any of my friends, and I didn't see any of his.

I did see his flat, though only very briefly while he collected his wallet, which he'd accidentally left behind. I did feel it was slightly strange, the way he hustled me out again, but I didn't say anything. I didn't question anything. I was still at the stage of absolute worship, when the object of one's affections can do no wrong.

But after that experience, I began to notice that Brian could be secretive. Although I was getting to know him really well, I couldn't help feeling he was keeping something from me.

The thought did cross my mind that he might be married, that there would be signs of another woman in his flat, or that her name might be on the door that he rushed me past, but I scotched that idea.

This was Brian, as honest as the day and completely reliable. Of course he wasn't married. So why did this feeling persist?

As with all good whirlwind romances, we knew in no time at all that we wanted to spend our lives together. Neither of us had mentioned marriage, but there was a kind of unspoken assumption.

I would have said yes on the spot had he asked, even with my worries about what he wasn't telling me.

In the end, of course, it had to come to light, and the timing of the revelation was not of Brian's choosing. It was as we emerged from the fish and chip shop and were heading for my flat to consume our respective suppers, that we heard a friendly male voice call after us.

"Hi, Doris. Long time no see."

Naturally, I assumed this was aimed at me and was a case of mistaken identity — not surprising in the gloom of a winter evening.

I was about to say, "Sorry, you've got the wrong person," but Brian responded. He raised his hand, called out an answer, and then hustled me off.

Sooner or later, I was going to have to ask for an explanation for the hustling. Once we were back in the flat, I decided that the moment had come.

"So why didn't you speak to your friend? You're not ashamed of me, are you, Brian?"

He was shocked.

"Of course not. How could you even think it?"

I straightened up with my back against the kitchen counter, where the two fish suppers lay emitting the most glorious fragrance, though not a romantic one, it has to be said. There is nothing glamorous about vinegar.

"I don't think it," I said. "Not really. But there's something going on here that I don't understand."

HE sighed, came towards me, and put his hands on my shoulders. "You're right. I haven't been completely honest with you." My heart sank. If he was about to mention the wife and three children, I didn't want to hear.

"It's about my name," he said.

I stared.

"Your name? What's wrong with it?"

"It's not what I said it was, and I didn't want to spoil things before we even got started. That's why I haven't invited you to the flat, just in case you see something that — well, just in case. And that's why I didn't introduce you to Jim outside the chip shop."

I smiled slowly.

"You've got a funny name?"

"No. But you will have if you marry me."

I stared again.

"Really?"

"My name isn't Brian Davidson. It's Brian Day."

There was a pause.

"Nickname Doris?"

He nodded, and after a moment's reflection about what my married name would be, I started to laugh.

"I don't think my parents would ever have thought of that. But I think it's lovely."

So he hugged me, and asked me properly if I would marry him, and naturally I said yes.

And suddenly the smell of vinegar seemed quite romantic after all. ■

Illustration by
Mike Heslop.

The

Bonfire Society

by Alison Carter.

A REN'T some of the people in this village extraordinary?" Tara beckoned her husband over to the window. "That chap walks by every evening at exactly eight-thirty. He's always chatting to himself."

Giles pulled aside the muslin curtain.

"You're right. He doesn't seem to come out at any other time. We're going to have to get used to some . . . characters, now we're living the rural life."

"But you're glad we moved out of London?"

Giles scanned the high street, lined with historic houses and trees bending over the road. Beyond, the street-light glinted on the pond, which lay at the edge of a large common.

"Yes, of course I am. I can walk out of my house and be in real countryside in five minutes. Fabulous."

Tara sipped her glass of wine.

"I'm not sure about the whole 'village life' thing, though. A woman came to the door last week asking if I wanted to be on the village hall booking rota. Something about looking after the book and taking calls."

"Really? Take care, my darling. You'll be carrying a basket full of jam and riding an ancient bicycle before the year is out. I'll have to leave you for a more up-to-date model."

Tara laughed.

"You wouldn't dare. She was a very charming woman, actually. But don't worry, Giles, I do not plan to immerse myself in fêtes and the church roof fund. I have enough on my hands getting this house under control."

"So what did you tell the charming woman?"

"I said I had to talk to you because we always decide on commitments jointly."

"I see. Well, I am definitely not the jam-making or village hall type. I should politely decline if I were you."

Giles and Tara Ransom had bought Lavingbury House less than two months before. After deciding to leave London for a quieter life and the possibility of starting a family, they had fallen in love with the early Tudor mansion as soon as they saw it. The previous owners, a couple in their sixties, had moved, the estate agent said, into a newer, smaller house in the village, something a little easier to maintain.

"They don't seem to have done so very much maintaining here," Tara had said on moving day, as a chest of drawers dislodged a lump of crumbling plaster, revealing the lathes beneath. "Certainly not for a while. But I plan to return this house to all its former glory."

Each evening, Tara gave her husband a full report.

"Giles, I have to find someone to help with the cleaning! My card's been in the village shop window for weeks, with no replies. I had no idea how challenging the house was going to be.

"I thought it would be an ideal position — *reliable cleaning help required for local couple.*"

"Ah." Giles held up a finger. "I guess we don't qualify as 'local' yet, darling. Perhaps that's the problem."

Tara walked out into the hall and came back with a stack of leaflets and cards.

"If we got involved in half the things that get pushed through the door we couldn't help but be local. The previous owners have left us some, too. Look." She handed leaflets over one at a time.

"Cricket team, neighbourhood watch, tidy-the-village day, Christmas fair, Scouts, Brownies, parish council, village hall film night, madrigals. Women's Institute, whist." Tara drew breath. "I could go on."

Giles backed away comically.

"Stop! You're frightening me!"

"I'm simply not the community type. Too many years in an anonymous city."

THE next morning, Tara answered a firm knock on the door.

A very small woman stood outside, holding a bulging folder.

"Good morning," she said. "Welcome to the village, Mrs Ransom. It's good to have some new young blood." Her voice was enormous for such a slight frame.

Tara was taken aback.

"It's, er, very kind of you, Mrs . . .?"

"Tomkins. Eva Tomkins. Parish clerk. May I come in?"

"Yes, of course." Tara stepped aside and Mrs Tomkins marched into the spacious hall.

"It's such a charming house," she said, looking around with satisfaction at the beams and flagged floor. "Quite the pride of the village. The historical society has masses of information about it, as I'm sure you know."

I missed the historical society, Tara thought wryly, from my list of village institutions.

"I don't know as much as I should," she said. "Any information would be helpful in the proposed work."

"Ah, yes, such a house needs a great deal of love. Harry and Liz stayed as long as they could."

"The previous owners?"

"Yes, indeed. And it's rather on that subject that I've called round." Mrs Tomkins opened her folder and smiled brightly. "Bonfire Night."

"Bonfire Night?"

"Yes. You see, this house has been the meeting point for the procession for so long that we know you will consider continuing the tradition. It's the position, you see, right at the head of the high street. And its age."

A faint memory came to Tara, of the only time she had met the previous owners, Mr and Mrs Bryant. They had talked about Sussex Bonfire Societies, and Tara and Giles had been unable to work out why it was such a major concern. Now, she could see, she was about to find out.

"Well, I'm not sure . . ."

"Such a wonderful evening. Everybody piles in here for treacle toffee and mulled wine . . ."

"Everyone?"

MRS TOMKINS looked surprised.

"Well, yes, dear. I don't know anyone who doesn't come to Bonfire Night. There are hundreds of visitors from outside, but only the Bonfire Society, the parish council and all the helpers come in here to liaise. Anyone who does the work. So, as I said, toffee and wine. Oh, of course, Lydia Mendoza introduced garlic bread last year, but Lydia is rather eccentric like that."

"Garlic bread." Tara was confused.

"Oh, dear me, you won't be expected to provide the toffee, or the wine, and certainly not the garlic bread." Mrs Tomkins laughed. "There's a committee. Of course, we'd appreciate the use of your Aga, but apart from that you can just . . . mingle."

"Has Lavingbury House always been the . . . centre of things?"

"For as long as I can remember, and I assure you that's quite some time! After the refreshments here, the society fetch the torches and the guy — it's a good ten feet tall, and where they find the material to dress it in 1605 style each year, I certainly don't know. The procession kicks off at eight and makes its way to the common for fireworks." She leaned towards Tara.

"We pride ourselves, Mrs Ransom, on our pyrotechnics in Lavingbury. I think you will be impressed."

Tara hesitated. The thought of most of the population of the village in her house on a dark, damp November night filled her with consternation. She didn't know any of them, and the mud! But she was anxious not to be rude.

"November the fifth — that's scarcely three weeks away," she said uncertainly. "We're hardly unpacked, to be frank. I don't . . ."

Mrs Tomkins smiled kindly.

"There is absolutely no ceremony, Mrs Ransom. Not a bit. Lavingbury is simply not smart. One year, Liz did the Bonfire Meeting when the roof was half off for repair. And her predecessor always seemed to have had a baby just before Guy Fawkes, and she just told us all to make the kitchen our own while she sat and nursed. Very relaxed! It's a chance for the whole village to get together."

Tara made an attempt to change the subject.

"There seem to be a number of village events, Mrs Tomkins. I was telling my husband about the film nights, and the fair, and the clean-ups. He was fascinated."

Mrs Tomkins smiled broadly.

"I am delighted he's so keen. Let your husband know that I can always be contacted at the parish office. We do need a co-ordinator for —"

"Oh, Mrs Tomkins," Tara interrupted before the clerk could appoint Giles to a committee in his absence, "I haven't offered you any tea."

"No need," she replied amiably. "I must dash. Lots of business. Think it over."

Mrs Tomkins grasped the iron handle of the front door and looked back at Tara.

"You will adore Bonfire Night."

Herbal

Garlic

WE'VE all seen the films where the only way to ward off a vampire is to wear cloves of garlic around your neck. But did you realise that the reason garlic was thought to be so powerful was because it was relied on so heavily by our forefathers in early medicine?

Everyone knows what garlic is — a member of the onion family that is used in cooking for a strong, distinctive flavouring. Did you know that it was also used by herbalists from the tenth century onwards and was thought to help cure a variety of ailments?

Garlic was used to treat bronchitis and asthma, and was also a traditional treatment for several types of parasites, including roundworm and tapeworm.

THAT night, Tara related the encounter to Giles.

"How numerous are the good folk of Lavingbury, anyway?"

Tara's eyes widened.

"Do you know, I haven't a clue."

"I don't suppose many of them are . . . very like us. We're hopeless city types, frankly, lacking stout shoes and unable to survive without e-mail."

"I don't know what we'll talk about."

Giles looked thoughtful.

"Obviously being a complete killjoy is just unpleasant. I might consider a bit of gentle cricket, come the summer. But socialising with the whole village? I can't say it sounds tempting."

The characters that they met that weekend rather confirmed Tara and Giles's belief that the Bonfire Night bash might be best avoided.

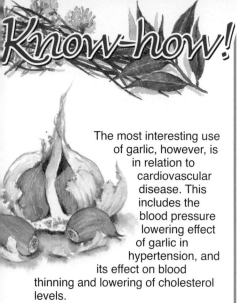

Buying a Sunday paper in the village shop, they were assailed by an earnest young man in a waxed coat asking them what they thought of a new building development.

An elderly lady bemoaned the suffering (with gout) of her black Labrador; she had it, along with three others, in the shop on leads.

They had almost escaped the shop when a lanky child with sticking-up hair stood in front of them.

"'Scuse me, but are you the new people at the big house?"

Giles peered at him.

"Well, I suppose we are."

"Should be good this year. Seen the wood pile already?" And he ran off.

Tara and Giles wandered down to the common, greeted by polite "good mornings" on the way. And there was indeed a huge pile of firewood — old chairs, a garden bench, a wardrobe and most of a fence.

"It's going to be quite a blaze," Giles said admiringly.

"And if we can sneak down here and enjoy it without having to host the event, it should be fun," Tara put in.

Giles gave a smug smile.

"I put a solid donation in the Bonfire Society box at the bakery."

Tara grinned.

"Good. Can we say we've done our bit, then?"

B UT it was not to be. Over the next fortnight, Mrs Tomkins was joined by several other parish council officials, members of the public and random children in discussing the meeting as though it were definitely taking place at Lavingbury House.

"It's your super front window, Mrs Ransom, of course," a Mr Carse said. He'd introduced himself as the village hall caretaker as Tara queued in front of him at the post office. "The perfect place to watch the torches if it's chilly. There's quite a bit of jostling, I can tell you."

Mrs Tomkins called again one evening. Tara wondered later whether it had been a deliberate move, making sure that she would find them both at home together so that they couldn't pass the buck.

"The caretaker said you had such a nice chat about Bonfire Night," she began.

"Um, yes. He's very nice."

"Mr Carse has been building that bonfire for forty-three years. He's a thoroughly kind individual." Mrs Tomkins looked thoughtful. "Doesn't like change, though. I don't know what he'd say about an alternative venue for the meeting."

Tara and Giles saw a ray of hope.

"What, Mrs Tomkins, would have been the alternative venue, if we had been reluctant?"

The little lady looked momentarily puzzled.

"Oh, I don't know. Nobody had got that far." She grinned. "Anyway, don't need to worry about that now!"

"Nobody," Giles said dryly when he'd shut the front door, "had got that far. Never mind. I'm sure it will be fine. We can bluff our way through in the conversational topics of feed prices and bake sales, darling."

"And you can impress the village children with your new computer."

NOVEMBER the fifth was clear and cold.

"The perfect night for fireworks," Mrs Tomkins said as she followed her husband into the kitchen of Lavingbury House. They carried boxes of glasses.

Mr Tomkins shook Tara and Giles's hands warmly.

"Welcome to the village, and many thanks for the continued use of the house for the meeting. Hope you enjoy yourselves."

Within an hour, the house was buzzing with all age groups and every walk of life. The front door never seemed to be shut, but Giles found he didn't need to keep adding wood to the big grate — someone always got there before him.

A delicious-looking fruit cake appeared on the kitchen table, compliments, Mrs Tomkins said, of the Bonfire Society ladies' group. And bottles of excellent red wine arrived by the Aga in a seemingly constant stream. Tara and Giles couldn't help but be impressed.

"The people here know their grapes," Giles said quietly to his wife. "No rubbish for the mulled wine."

Tara got into conversation with a tall, ruddy-faced man of about forty-five, dressed in sagging yellow corduroy.

"So," she said, "do you live in the village centre or outside? One of the farms, perhaps?"

He laughed heartily.

"Farming! Goodness, no. I don't know a cow from a field of oats. No, I'm a website designer — and, far more importantly, I'm a football coach to all

132

ages, for my sins."

"Website design?" Tara's eyebrows lifted. "I'm thinking about starting a little business, once I've got the lion's share of work on the house done. Do you take on that sort of thing?"

"I certainly do." He fished a card from a capacious pocket. "John Denham."

Tara looked at the smart, modern design. There was I, she mused, reckoning he was a slow-thinking man of the soil!

Giles was watching out of the big front window for the arrival of the guy when a tall lady in tweed approached.

"Jolly good of you," she said in a hearty voice, "to let us all pile in again. Don't know what we would have done otherwise. I'm Camilla Bamforth." She shook Giles's hand firmly.

"We're delighted," Giles replied. "It must be a good spot for the firework display, such a large common."

"It is. But actually the chaps could set up their display on a ten foot square, they're so experienced. But yes, the common is marvellous — plenty of space."

Giles smiled.

"Fêtes, cricket, that sort of thing."

"I was thinking more of the teen shelter and the skate park."

Giles was momentarily speechless.

"Skate park?"

Mrs Bamforth nodded vigorously.

"We've had so little for young people in the past. They tended to escape the village as fast as they could. Parents — well, all of us — we wanted them safe and we wanted them here. It's taken a great deal of negotiation, and a great deal of fund-raising, but by the spring our young people should have a place to hang out and a rather nifty skate park, for inline skating and boards."

"I see," Giles said.

THE torches and the guy arrived, followed by crowds of villagers in scarves and fleeces, or the famous striped costume of the Bonfire Society. It was a thrilling sight, the air hot with the flames, and sparks dancing into the black sky.

The pavement outside the house moved with families greeting each other as they made their way to the common, small children high on their dads' shoulders.

Tara stood by her front door waiting for the last of those inside to leave. A woman in a padded coat came out and stood beside her, looking happily at the passing people.

"I love this night so much. It's what village life is all about."

"Yes, it's great. I'm Tara Ransom."

"I know. It's not such a big place, Lavingbury. Certainly not as big as it looks tonight."

They stood for a moment longer.

"You'll be wanting someone to help you around the house, I imagine, Mrs Ransom? Lavingbury House doesn't clean itself."

"It doesn't." Tara turned to her. "So you might be willing to . . . ?"

"I run a small company. There are so many tasks that need doing in the village — we've got busy mums, elderly people keen to stay in their own homes, all sorts. We provide a flexible service. I'm Jan." The woman produced a card and handed it to Tara.

"I hadn't had the opportunity of meeting you until today, although we used to help Liz in the house. But village gatherings are such a good way of networking. Face to face is best.

"Oh, there's my husband. It was nice to meet you at last." And Jan vanished into the crowd.

Giles and Tara locked up and followed the gently moving crowd to the common, where the fireworks were breathtaking. They stood arm in arm by the enormous bonfire, watching small children throw sticks from a distance or become sticky eating toffee apples.

IT began to drizzle and they made their way back to the house. There they stood in the beautiful bay window and watched the stragglers wandering home.

"I met some fascinating people tonight," Giles said.

Tara nodded.

"Me, too. Do you know the WI are working on a village plan for tackling climate change? I had a talk with one of the members."

"Somehow it doesn't surprise me," Giles replied.

"I've got two business cards here," Tara said.

"I can top that with three." Giles patted his upper pocket, and then smiled at a pair of children on the opposite pavement squabbling over a hot dog.

"What a place," he said quietly.

"What a surprise." Tara drew her cardi around her. "I feel a bit humbled, don't you?"

"We got a few things wrong. Is there any more mulled wine?"

"Have a look."

Giles went through to the kitchen and returned empty-handed.

"The whole place is immaculate. How many of our visitors must have worked on clearing that kitchen before we left for the fireworks?"

"This neighbourly thing," Tara said quietly. "This community spirit. It's a whole new area for me."

"Yes," Giles said, pulling his wife gently towards him. "But, do you know, I think I'm really going to enjoy it." ∎

Illustration by William Webb.

Creating A Stir!

by Mary Kettlewell.

N EXT Sunday is Harvest Festival, and we need more help with the decorating." Reverend Tim Hawthorne beamed hopefully at the congregation. "Any time on Saturday morning."

I rather fancied the idea. I'd decorated plenty of canvasses, birthday cards and posters at art college. I'd even painted my bicycle pink, with red, yellow, blue and orange flowers all over the frame. But decorating a mediaeval church? That really would be something.

So that's how I found myself trooping into St Carrog's on a warm autumn morning with a group of ladies carrying flowers, ribbons of greenery, buckets, scissors and vases, whilst their husbands staggered along behind laden with marrows, cucumbers, swedes, parsnips, apples and pears.

I smiled at the woman next to me.

"Candy Arkwright. I'm new to the job."

She gave me a funny look, which wasn't surprising. I was clutching an enormous bunch of seaweed, a pailful of shells, three weirdly shaped chunks of driftwood, two stranded starfish and a child's shrimping net.

Professor Laura Steiffel, my tutor, had drummed her mantra into us students on our first day at art college.

"You're here to challenge, create and shock."

So that's what I had decided to do.

"The Fish Harvest," I said cheerfully to my fellow volunteer. "You know, fishermen harvesting the seas off our coasts in foul weather and fine."

My neighbour smiled warily.

"Very nice, dear." I could see nudges and whispers in the group around me. Clearly they thought I was beyond hope.

Once inside the cool church, my eyes alighted on the font. Just the job! It would make a brilliant setting for my Fish Harvest. I set down my load of seaweed and began to drape fronds of it round the stone base. Soon, a faintly fishy smell began to mingle with the ancient stones and last week's incense.

I'd just fastened a piece of driftwood in place when a discreet cough sounded behind me.

"Er, I hope you don't mind, dear," an elderly volunteer said softly, "but Mrs Bracewell's been doing the font for years."

Before I could answer, the sound of heels could be heard clattering down the aisle. Firm, determined heels.

"What on earth's that?" a voice exclaimed sharply.

An austere looking lady, dressed in sensible tweed skirt and no-nonsense blouse and waistcoat, was pointing to the seaweed with a pair of kitchen scissors.

"Bladderwrack," I said weakly.

"Bladderwrack, girl? Good heavens!"

"You must be Mrs Bracewell." I stretched out a hand. "Candy Arkwright. I'm an art student and this is the beginnings of my Fish Harvest," I said tentatively.

To my relief the scissors drooped.

"That explains it all."

"What explains what, Mrs Bracewell?"

"Art students. They're all crazy. Men with ponytails. Girls with torn clothing. Painting dustbins and pickling dead animals." She sniffed. "And no morals!"

I wondered whether to give an indignant reply or laugh. Then I noticed the humorous glint in her eyes, so I laughed.

"You've got a point. But we work hard, too. I'm up to the neck in my finals." I removed a strand of seaweed from the font and threw it into my basket. "I had no idea this was your space. I'll pull it off and start somewhere else."

"You'll do nothing of the sort. St Carrog's needs stirring up. We're turning into a load of old fogeys here. Now tell me all about this bladderwrack."

"It's going to be a collage of seaweed, driftwood, a shrimping net and . . . maybe a backdrop using a chart of the North Sea."

"That's what I like about you youngsters. Full of imagination. But you need fish. Masses of them."

"Fish? But they'd smell awful, and they're incredibly expensive."

"Not flesh and blood ones. Wooden fish! I've got a boxful at home. They appear every time the grandchildren turn up."

I pictured fish peeping out from the seaweed with tiny black eyes.

"That would be great. Can I borrow them?"

"Of course. I'll be in all afternoon. I live in Chesil Cottage, just by the footbridge across the river."

"I still feel bad about pinching your space, Mrs Bracewell."

She laid a hand on my arm.

"Don't. I'll fill the west window with arum lilies instead. They make people feel faint, you know. It's the sickly smell."

She grinned mischievously.

"It'll spruce up the vicar's sermon, having half the congregation passing out!" Then she strode away and disappeared through the west door.

MY brother wasn't using his old red van that afternoon so I borrowed it and drove to Chesil Cottage. I expected Mrs Bracewell to answer the door in her sensible tweeds.

Instead, I was greeted by a tall man with gelled hair and baggy clothes. The wide brown eyes and full mouth nearly made me forget what I'd come for.

"Er, it's the fish."

He glanced at the van and nodded.

"Ah, I'll tell my aunt." He turned round and called to the back of the cottage. "Fishmonger, Aunt Eleanor."

"See if there's any smoked haddock, Julian."

He smiled and I wished I'd worn something decent.

"Any luck with smoked haddock?"

"No, not fresh fish. The wooden fish."

He put one hand on the pillar of the porch and stared at me, puzzled.

"Let's start from square one. You're selling wooden fish?"

I was beginning to feel like Alice in Wonderland.

"I'm not the fishmonger. I'm decorating the church with a fish harvest theme and Mrs Bracewell . . . your aunt . . . said I could borrow her grandchildren's wooden fish."

"This is getting more and more interesting. Tell me all about your Fish Harvest."

I didn't have a chance, because Mrs Bracewell's voice floated out from the kitchen.

"Julian, what on earth are you playing at out there?"

"It's a girl come for some wooden fish."

"Ask her in then. Don't keep her on the doorstep!"

Julian stood to one side and gestured.

"Come on in, please. It seems you've passed the test."

Mrs Bracewell was busy peeling an enormous pile of apples.

"Chutney for the harvest auction. Have you two met properly? Candy, this is my nephew, Julian, who drops in when he fancies a weekend of free meals. And Julian, meet Candy. She's an art student who pinched my time-honoured place in church for her Fish Harvest."

Julian laughed.

"She must be brave if she's had the bottle to cross you, Aunt!"

I was beginning to like Julian and his aunt. I could see how fond they were of each other, and their cheerful humour was a tonic.

Mrs Bracewell took a toy box out of the cupboard.

"There's enough fish here to burst the net."

Julian stepped forward.

"I'll give you a hand to carry them to your van. The box will be heavy."

There were no flies on Mrs Bracewell's nephew, that was for sure. The box of fish must have weighed all of two pounds!

Now, artwork is very personal. And normally if somebody had offered to help I would have given a firm "no". But Julian was different. Not only was he good looking, he had that laid-back air of confidence that I like in a man. So, when he offered, I told a white lie.

"Thanks," I said, trying to sound as demure as possible. "I could do with some help."

An hour later, Julian stood back, head on one side, admiring our handiwork.

"Talent, Candy. Sheer brilliance. That's what we've got here." He peered at the arrangement. "But you know what I think? It needs a few more fronds of seaweed to finish it off."

In fact, there was more than enough seaweed already. But Julian was clearly angling for an afternoon on the beach with me, and I had to admit it, the idea was decidedly appealing. Then came my second white lie of the afternoon.

"Yes, I suppose it does look a bit skimpy."

We drove in my brother's van along a sandy lane with seagulls wheeling

Wade Brig And Birks, Aberfeldy

MY late husband, Alistair, was born at 14, Chapel Street, Aberfeldy. He served his pharmacy apprenticeship with W.L. McNaughton and his parents ran the newsagents during the 1930s and 40s.

I spent many lovely holidays there. It was such a peaceful haven compared to war-ravaged London.

I now live in Australia, but during a trip back to Britain my sister and I spent ten days touring Scotland and managed to make it to Aberfeldy, where I found the Birks as beautiful as ever.

— *Mrs A.McG., NSW, Australia.*

J. CAMPBELL KERR.

overhead. There was an outcrop of rock on the beach and I knew just what would happen. I was right, too.

"It's a bit slippery here. You'd better hang on to my hand." So there I was holding Julian's hand, a mere hour and three quarters after turning up on Mrs Bracewell's doorstep.

✳   ✳   ✳   ✳

All too soon it was over. I had to return to my art classes and Julian, in the words of his aunt, was "all hyped-up for one of his globe-trotting jaunts as a botanist." I went with him to the station and he held my hand until the train drew out.

"Take care, Candy. I'll miss you. We'll meet up when I get back." But I'd heard that before. A couple of weeks in South America for Julian and I'd be past history.

I threw myself into the term's work, said "yes" to every guy who asked me out on a date and went to every student party. But I couldn't forget the man with the wide-eyed smile and warm, strong hands.

THE Christmas break came and, one day, my doorbell rang. There, out of the blue, was Julian.

"Candy, you're looking lovely."

I couldn't believe my eyes. Julian stood in front of me, with the same warm smile. I searched for words.

"You . . . you've been in the sun."

"Ecuador."

"Did you have a good trip?"

"Terrible. My sleeping tablets didn't work, the jungle was hot and full of mosquitoes and there weren't any fish and chip shops."

I invited him in and we sat in the kitchen whilst the kettle boiled.

"So, not a successful trip?" I said, breaking an uncomfortable silence between us.

"Only one thing kept me going . . ."

I fully expected him to say "the beer" or "the women", but I was wrong.

"It was the thought of you, Candy."

I felt myself blushing.

"I kept wanting to e-mail, telephone and write letters, Candy, but I knew it would make the pain worse, knowing I couldn't be near you."

"Julian," I said weakly. "I'm going to do another decoration in church. I've been given a spare key, will you help me?"

"Just try to keep me away." He smiled broadly.

The next day, Aunt Eleanor greeted us with bear hugs all round.

"So it's stood the test of time, has it?" She chuckled. "Absence makes the heart grow fonder."

"Ecuador was awful," Julian muttered.

"And so was college," I said.

She sighed.

"The pain of love. What it is to be young."

After our third cup of tea and countless biscuits, we said goodbye to Aunt Eleanor and headed to the church, where we opted for cotton-wool and polystyrene angels, white with silver haloes, blowing golden trumpets.

As I fastened them to the font, Julian's face was inches from mine. Cool it, Candy, I thought to myself, and threw out an everyday question just to let things simmer down.

"All this flying off to exotic places — is that to do with your job as a botanist?"

"No! I'm really a smuggler, bringing in jewels and drink at the dead of night from far-flung places. It's a great life."

"I don't believe a word of it." I laughed. "Where's the black stubble and eyepatch? Anyway, you're not sinister enough."

"No, you're right. I'm not in the piracy league. I'm in charge of the orchid house at the Subtropical Gardens near Foley, hence the trips abroad.

"I love the work. It's a real adrenalin shot when you've been tending a rare variety for months with no joy and then suddenly it blooms."

"I can understand that. It's like chucking out three messed up canvasses and then all at once, bingo, you get it right."

"Any plans for after college, Candy?"

"I fancy advertising — designing those eye-stoppers you see on roadside hoardings."

"Big, bold and brassy." Julian laughed.

I stared at him in pretend disgust.

"I hope you're not talking about me."

This time there wasn't any jokiness in his reply.

"If it were you, I'd have put it this way: pretty and slender, with a lovely sense of humour."

He leaned over the font, his lips brushing mine. But at that instant the church door opened and the decorating ladies trooped in laden with holly, ivy, Christmas tree lights and lilies. Reluctantly, I picked up the tape and began to fasten Gabriel, Raphael and Michael to the font.

When Julian left me that afternoon he said something I've treasured ever since.

"Me growing orchids, you painting pictures — that makes us soulmates, Candy. We're both working towards something beautiful, something to light up the world."

✳   ✳   ✳   ✳

Spring came, and Julian flew in from New Guinea. Later, he kissed me in the dilapidated old summerhouse in Aunt Eleanor's garden.

We would have stayed there all evening if it hadn't been for Aunt Eleanor, bringing out a tray of tea.

Soon, the lupins were awash with butterflies and Aunt Eleanor's sixtieth birthday was looming. She zoomed off to London for a fortnight's holiday with her sister, laden down with suitcases.

"What shall we give her, Julian? She's been so kind and welcoming."

"Tricky. She always wanted a conservatory built on to the cottage." He smiled ruefully. "Unfortunately, my savings are at an all-time low at the moment."

"And all I have is a student loan."

The Fall

AS daylight's hours begin to wane,
So autumn's sweet caress
Transforms the trees to russet flame,
As her gentle breath
Carries on a silken breeze
O'er fields of golden grain,
Awakening the little flowers
Refreshed by fragrant rain.
Apples now with crimson blush
Dance high upon the boughs,
Blackberries in thorny crush
Tempt hungry, wild mouths.
The landscape starts to alter,
As gilt leaves ebb and flow,
Falling from the treetops
Like flakes of golden snow.
— *Clare Allen.*

"So that's that," he said.

"Not quite. I've got an idea. This ramshackle old summerhouse . . ."

We worked furiously. Julian slaved away with crosscut saws, nails, wood filler, screwdrivers and chisels, cutting out the rotten wood and raising the flagging roof.

Then I piled in with acrylics and brushes, Professor Steiffel's words tumbling through my head.

"Create! Paint! Shock!"

By the end of day three, a florid-faced Adam and a white-skinned Eve, both discreetly draped, were peering out from a hedge of red, yellow, purple and scarlet tropical flowers.

A sky-blue river full of bulging-eyed frogs meandered round the four walls. Exotic birds with absurdly long beaks fluttered cheerfully and a crocodile with a wicked glint surveyed a hippo basking peacefully in a pond.

In short, Aunt Eleanor's shed had become a garden of Eden. The birthday present received its last lick of paint and final nail two hours before the London train arrived.

Her face was a picture when she saw it.

"Candy, you're a genius. It's absolutely spectacular . . . out of this world."

"Julian did the fiddly bits, knocking in the nails and planing wood."

"Then you're both geniuses. Or should it be genii?" Before we knew where we were she had gathered us up into an all-embracing cuddle.

She decided to have a celebration a fortnight later.

"We'll throw a party to christen the summerhouse. We'll invite the vicar, the flower ladies, that young couple from next door and old Major Petherton.

142

Glen Lyon.

It might cheer the old misery up."

Her eyes twinkled.

"Can vicars christen summerhouses if they're Gardens of Eden? I'll have to ask Mr Hawthorne." She rambled on blissfully. "We'll need plenty of nibbles: olives and feta cheese, taramasalata, aubergine dip . . ."

My abiding memory of that party is of Aunt Eleanor dressed in a gorgeous silk frock and floral hat, taking the vicar's arm and leading him on a tour of the Garden of Eden.

"Have another red pepper and caramelised onion vol-au-vent, Vicar, and I'll show you our splendid Eve. Don't worry, she's perfectly respectable!"

A month later, Julian led me out into the Garden of Eden under an orange harvest moon. He took my hand as we stood close to the tropical flowers, watching a hedgehog bumbling across the lawn.

"It is not good for man to be alone," he said softly.

I remembered the words from long ago in Miss Trueblood's Sunday School class.

"God spoke those words in the Garden of Eden."

"It's me speaking, too, Candy."

"You needn't be alone any more, Julian. Not now." And I held him tight.

✳   ✳   ✳   ✳

Aunt Eleanor threw a spectacular reception for us in the Garden of Eden in late spring. Mr Hawthorne married us and the whole street came to share it with us. My bouquet was a mixture of pink and white cherry blossom, intertwined with the delicate fronds of dulse – well, I just had to have seaweed, didn't I? Just for old times' sake. ▪

So Far From Home

L AUREN glanced through the aeroplane window at the vista below. She saw grey-green fields dotted with sheep, rocky outcroppings leading to an unforgiving shoreline and a flat, slate-blue sea.

"Welcome to the Falkland Islands."

The pilot, part of the military outposting, smiled at her. Lauren smiled back, though her stomach suddenly seethed with nerves.

What was she doing?

It had seemed like such a good idea last summer, when her job as a primary school teacher had grown far too familiar and dull, her last single friend had married, and life seemed to stretch in an endless, unwavering line. She'd wanted change — adventure.

And here it was! All the adventure she could possibly want, stretching out below her in all of its bleak glory.

The plane landed on the airfield with a little bump, and Lauren gathered her things. One of the

Illustration by David McAllister.

teachers was meeting her to accompany her to her provided accommodation in Stanley, the islands' only town.

"Do you know it takes four weeks by ship to get to the Falklands?" her best friend, Kelly, had demanded when Lauren had told her she was planning to take up a position as a travelling teacher with the Islands' Camp Education Unit.

"Yes, but there are planes now," Lauren had replied dryly, "and it's only ten hours to Santiago."

"Lauren, you'll be moving eight thousand miles away," Kelly had continued desperately. "Do you know how far away that is? Have you looked on the map?"

Yes, she had. When the position had come up, she'd traced a line from the tip of South America to the tiny islands dotting the edge of the page, the edge of the world.

"It won't be for ever."

144

Lauren had no idea how long she would stay. Perhaps it would be for ever.

Her ties to England were tenuous at best, now that her parents had passed away. She was an only child, and her friends were all pairing off and having children.

This was what she needed.

Except that now, as she stepped out of the plane into a chill, salty wind, despite the fact that it was January and mid-summer here, she wasn't so sure.

"Welcome to the Falklands!"

Marie Bryson, a fellow teacher, red-cheeked and swathed in a huge parka, stepped forward.

"You must be exhausted. I can take you to your flat right now, and you can have a rest."

Lauren piled her things into the Land-Rover, barely registering the rocky scenery and rutted, gravel road as they drove from the airstrip into Stanley.

She forced herself to admire the few buildings huddled

by Katharine Swartz.

against the shore. A huge whalebone memorial stood outside Stanley's Anglican church, a surprisingly impressive structure built in the Victorian age.

"The new vicar just arrived last month," Marie informed her. "He's settling in well — a single man." Her eyes twinkled knowingly, and Lauren made a non-committal sound. She hadn't come here to meet somebody, though she already suspected the islands' small population was full of well-meaning matchmakers.

Her flat was in a building that housed many of the school and travelling unit's teachers, and Lauren duly expressed her gratitude at the small, sparsely furnished space.

Someone had thought to put milk and butter in the fridge, and there was a little tin of coffee as well as a covered dish for supper.

"You're all so kind," she said, and teetering on the brink of exhaustion, she fell into a deep sleep as soon as Marie had said goodbye.

Her first few weeks in Stanley were a blur. As part of the Camp Education Unit, she broadcast lessons and homework assignments by radio each morning to the outlying sheep stations, known simply as "camp". For two weeks out of every six, she would travel by plane to the camp settlement and give individual lessons to the children there.

Then there was the flurry of meeting everyone in Stanley, the teachers and shopkeepers, the bush pilots and radio controller, and of course Dan.

DAN PETTY was the new minister Marie had mentioned, and he stopped by Lauren's flat three days after she'd arrived, proffering a jar of honey and a packet of chocolate digestives.

"From home," he explained ruefully. "Sometimes it's hard to get things here."

"Why did you decide to come here?" Lauren asked after she'd made them both cups of coffee and opened the biscuits. They were sitting on the hard settee in her little lounge.

"I'm not sure, exactly," he said slowly. "I saw the advert — *Must be able to act on own initiative, like flying, and appreciate a hardy, rugged lifestyle* — and I wondered just what kind of person would take a job like that. Then I thought, well, maybe I would." He laughed. "Daft, isn't it?"

"Not that daft," Lauren replied with a smile. "I suppose I felt the same. There wasn't much keeping me in England, and there's something appealing about going so far away, finding adventure and all that."

"No-one keeping you at home, then?" Dan asked lightly, and Lauren shook her head.

"I'm not looking for a relationship," she said firmly. "I'm here for the experience and adventure."

He nodded, giving her a wry salute.

"Message received."

Lauren bit her lip. Her words had sounded harsher than she'd intended, but she decided not to correct Dan's impression. A relationship would complicate things, and what she'd said was true. Wasn't it?

They chatted for a few minutes about life in Stanley.

"The community here is very close, very warm," Dan said. "And when it becomes too close, you can always jump on a plane to camp and escape."

"You travel, too, don't you?"

"Yes, I fly to all the different camps once a month to help communion services. Do you know I'd never flown before coming here? Now I'm in one of those little planes as often as a car."

Over the next few weeks, Lauren found herself spending more and more time with Dan. As two of the few single people in Stanley, they were often thrown together.

Despite her earlier warning, it was inevitable, she supposed, that one of them would make something of it. She just hadn't expected it to be her.

Despite all her self-assurances that she'd come to the Falklands for experience and adventure, not romance, she found herself gazing at Dan in odd moments, noting the easy way he talked with everyone — young, old or crochety — wreathed in smiles. And for someone who had never flown before arriving, he seemed to take to the rugged lifestyle with a natural grace.

But he showed absolutely no interest in her as anything more than a friend. Why should he? She'd made her position abundantly clear.

She tried to broach the subject once, but soon lost her nerve.

"Did you leave anyone special at home?" she asked at a social after church.

"I wouldn't have come if I did," Dan replied cheerfully. "I'm not mad."

"No," she agreed with a little smile. "Of course, it's not easy to meet someone here, is it?"

"It will happen when it happens," Dan replied easily, before being distracted by another parishioner.

It was ridiculous to feel this way, Lauren told herself. Hadn't she been clear with Dan about why she was here? She'd come to find her independence, not love. Unfortunately, it seemed as if you couldn't choose what you'd find.

TWO months after Lauren arrived, she had her first camp visit. She would be spending two weeks at a camp on the other side of the island, near Goose Green. There were five families living there, and eight children under ten. Lauren could hardly wait for this new adventure.

Dan drove her to the airfield in his beaten old Rover. The road was bumpy, as were all of the islands' few roads, and Lauren found herself thrown against the doorframe or Dan on more than one occasion.

Laughing, he put his arm around her shoulder.

"I'll keep you steady," he said, and though there was nothing romantic about the strong arm holding her secure, Lauren wondered if another meaning laced his words.

Dan parked the car, releasing her easily, and disappointment flickered through her.

She shrugged it off. It hardly mattered now. She was flying to camp for two weeks, and when she returned Dan would be off on visits of his own.

"I'll see you next month," he promised as she was about to climb into the little plane. "Take care. These planes take a bit of getting used to."

"I know!" Lauren glanced at the seemingly flimsy craft and grimaced.

"Rubbish! She's as safe as one of your fancy jets," Will, the pilot, assured her. "Shall we go? Goose Green is waiting, and I heard on the radio that there's a storm brewing off the coast."

Camp, Lauren discovered, was a community in itself, with bunks, barns, a dining-hall and a large farmhouse. The children had been waiting eagerly for

Lauren's arrival, and were more than willing pupils.

Over a huge breakfast of eggs, bacon, sausage and fried bread, Rena Franklin, a farmer's wife and mother to two of Lauren's pupils, looked at her speculatively.

"What made a slip of a thing like you come all the way out here?"

Lauren laughed as she tucked into her breakfast.

"Everyone keeps saying that, but I suppose it's for the same reason as everyone else."

"Mmm." Rena took a sip of coffee. "You know, Michael and Ella's dad is a widower."

Lauren just managed to refrain from rolling her eyes.

"That's a shame," she said politely, and Rena chuckled.

"You mean it has nothing to do with you? It's hard to find a husband here, you know."

Herbal

Celery

YOU may think of celery as a food, but the stalks that we buy today in the supermarket are not the same plant that our ancestors grew. Italian farmers developed what we now call celery in the seventeenth century.

You may know that celery stalks are a healthy food, but did you know that the seeds are the part used in plant medicine? The seeds help rid the body of uric acid, which often causes pain and inflammation in gout and arthritis.

Celery is also thought to ease stomach pains, calm the mind and act as a diuretic. Just think, it does all that and can also help you lose weight if you eat it!

"Maybe I'm not looking," Lauren answered pertly, and Rena gave her a knowing glance.

"Not now, perhaps," she said, "but one day you will be."

Dan's face flashed through Lauren's mind. Perhaps Rena was right, although Lauren suspected that if she was looking, she'd already found him.

How could she tell Dan she'd changed her mind, when she didn't even know if he felt anything for her?

BACK in Stanley, Dan was gone for a fortnight of camp visits. Lauren tried to immerse herself in her work. It had taken her some time to become accustomed to broadcasting lessons on the radio, speaking slowly and clearly for an invisible audience, imagining them listening, anticipating any possible questions —

And missing Dan.

Due to different flying visits, their paths barely crossed until May, and the onset of winter. Although the temperature seldom dipped below freezing, the wind was still cold and bitter, the sky slate-grey and menacing with thick, heavy clouds.

Lauren was preparing to head out to another camp, this time a remote station on one of the smaller islands.

"I never seem to see you any more," Dan said ruefully, when he stopped by

Know-how!

her flat for a visit.

"We need to co-ordinate our schedules," Lauren joked, but Dan only frowned.

"That might not be a bad idea.

"May I drive you to the airport at least?" he asked. "Or have you already got a lift?"

"No, I'd love you to take me."

"Good."

They were both strangely silent on the bumpy ride to the airfield, and Lauren wondered if she was imagining the thread of tension between them.

As he parked the car, Dan smiled at her, but worry shadowed his eyes.

"Be careful, Lauren. Those clouds look dangerous."

"You're a worrier," Lauren teased. "I'll be fine."

He drummed his fingers on the steering wheel.

"I think we should talk when you return," he said abruptly. "I mean . . ." Now he looked at her, wry and hesitant. "It would be good to . . . have a chat."

"Yes, it would," she agreed, managing to keep her voice light. Her pulse thrummed in anticipation. "I'll be back in two weeks."

The journey to the remote camp was uneventful, despite the clouds. The weather, however, worsened over Lauren's fortnight away, so that when the time came for her departure, her pilot scanned the heavy sky with a frown.

"I don't like the look of those clouds."

"That's what Dan said, a fortnight ago." Despite her light tone, Lauren felt a pang of unease. Will was normally so confident about flying, but the look on his face showed foreboding.

"Should we wait?" she asked. After a long moment Will shook his head.

"No. They're moving eastward. We should be all right."

Nodding decisively, he helped Lauren into the plane.

The clouds and wind made the flight bumpier than usual, and Lauren clung to her armrest. As the turbulence increased, she noticed Will's strained, white face and felt the lurch of her own answering fear.

At that moment, Lauren felt she'd had all the adventure and experience she could possibly want. She realised it had only been foolish pride which had kept her from telling Dan how she felt.

"It's no good," Will called back to her. "We can't go on."

"What are you saying?" Fear made Lauren's voice quaver.

"I'll have to make an emergency landing. There's a small camp nearby. I'll try for their airstrip."

Lauren's eyes were tightly shut, her knuckles gripping the armrest white, as Will made his bumpy landing on the tiny airstrip.

When the plane finally shuddered to a stop, they both let out a weak laugh of relief.

"They'll have a good old worry over us," Will said ruefully. "We're supposed to land in Stanley this afternoon, and no-one will show."

"What will they think?" Lauren asked anxiously. What would Dan think?

"Hopefully, that we were sensible and stayed over somewhere. This storm shows no sign of stopping yet, and I don't think we'll be able to clear out of here until tomorrow, at the earliest."

THEY were cleared for flight the following afternoon, and Will radioed Stanley.

Lauren had never been so glad to see the now familiar buildings along the shore as they came in for landing. A cluster of people gathered by the edge of the airfield, and Lauren glimpsed Dan's old Rover.

Suddenly Dan himself was striding towards her. Before Lauren could even voice a greeting, he'd taken her by the shoulders.

"I thought I'd lost you," he said, and then his lips were on hers.

Lauren returned the kiss, at first with surprise and then with joy.

As he released her, she blinked up at him.

"I didn't think you cared . . ."

"I was trying to pretend I didn't. You made it clear you weren't interested in romance when we first met. I've been praying for you to change your mind!"

Lauren smiled.

"I changed my mind a long time ago. I'd decided to tell you when I got back to Stanley."

"And I beat you to it!" He put his arm around her shoulders, drawing her close.

Despite the cold wind rolling in from the sea, Lauren felt wonderfully warm and safe.

"You know what this means," she said as they walked towards Dan's Rover. "We are definitely going to have to co-ordinate our schedules!"

Dan dropped a kiss on the top of her head.

"You've got that right."

Lauren slid into the car. She was looking forward to getting back to her flat, her home. Somehow along the way, she realised, the Falklands had become home.

And so had Dan. ▨

Conkering Heroes!

by Kath Kilburn.

Illustration
by John
Hancock.

FINN! Wait for me!" Billy stumbled after Finn, his breathing short and rapid.

"Come on, Finn. Time to go home. We'll be in trouble."

"Aw . . ."

"Come on, time for tea."

They crept into the house and quickly washed their hands.

"Now then, boys." Maria Maguire, rounded and red-faced, bustled into the kitchen. "Billy, what were you doing keeping the lad out till this time? You know he has school tomorrow."

"Aye, Maria, it was foolish of me!" Billy, wiry as a whippet, exchanged furtive winks with his grandson.

Illustration
by Klim
Forster.

151

Finn laid his hand on top of the oven and yelped.

"Gran, what have you done? That's much too hot — they'll be ruined!"

Maria reached into her apron pocket and brought out five oversized conkers, shining like burnished fire irons.

"Are these what you're worried about?"

Finn's face lit up.

"Phew, thanks, Gran."

Finn took the conkers, but Maria hadn't finished.

"It's not enough, I suppose, that you try to put the vinegar back in the bottle when you've soaked those dirty things in it for hours. You then want to tie up the oven all afternoon, drying them out or whatever you're meant to be doing. Load of nonsense."

Finn paid no attention. He studied one of his treasures by the fading light.

"This one's going to be a fifty-niner at least, Grandad."

Billy smiled across at his wife.

"I should think so," he said.

It was tradition that, when Finn stayed with his grandparents, it was Billy who put the lad to bed. Maria might perform every other domestic task, but Billy and Finn enjoyed the few minutes they routinely spent ironing the creases out of the day with a nightly man to man chat — one young man snuggled under the duvet; one not so young man perching on the edge of the bed.

"Why doesn't Grandma rate conkers, Grandad? They're brilliant! But she doesn't think they're important."

"Oh, well, Finn, women are different from us. Your gran likes her crosswords and her knitting. She doesn't like anything you have to shake the muck off."

"Mum's not that interested, either." Finn grinned. "It's always Dad who takes me to collect them. Well, it used to be — we used to go to the park where the big horse chestnuts are."

Billy rearranged Finn's bedclothes so the little boy was tucked in tight.

"And you will do again, as soon as the baby's born and you're all settled back at home. Everything will be back to normal then."

"I don't know whether Dad will have time," Finn said quietly. "Mum says babies are a lot of work. He might have to help Mum a lot with my new brother."

"Or sister!" Billy put in.

Finn pulled a face but said nothing.

"He'll still have time for you, Finn," his grandad said reassuringly. "You mark my words."

＊　＊　＊　＊

The next day Finn seemed in high spirits as he joined his gran in the playground after school.

"Grandad and I need to practise with the conkers tonight, Gran. There's a tournament coming up — our school against St Agatha's — it's part of the half-term fun day. We're doing loads of daft games and my teacher's going to have wet sponges thrown at him! But the conkers will be best — we're bound to win." Finn looked hopefully at his gran. "Do you think Mum will be able to come to watch?"

Maria hesitated.

"I think we'd better wait and see, Finn. But Grandad and I can come, can't we? We'll enjoy it."

"Yes, of course," he said quickly. "I meant you as well."

One of Grandma's special teas — corned beef hash followed by apple pie — was bolted down by the two pals before they set off to find yet more conkers for soaking, stringing and shining to iron hardness.

They returned home two hours later, dishevelled and scratched, with a carrier bag full, ready for attention next day.

Conkerers of both generations fell into bed early that night, exhausted from their pursuit of the perfect specimen.

Billy was yawning as Maria snuggled under the eiderdown beside him.

"You're as daft as an eight-year-old yourself, Billy Maguire," she muttered, with a smile.

"Aye, you're probably right," Billy agreed, rubbing his eyes. "But the lad's having a good time — that's the important thing right now."

＊　＊　＊　＊

"Grandad?" Finn was helping Billy at his allotment the following evening. The conkers were shut up in a kitchen cupboard, safe from any neighbourhood rivals.

"Yes?"

"Do you think girls can ever be as good as boys? Say, with conkers? Or cars? Do they ever like trains and stuff? Boys don't like dolls and all that dressing up, do they?"

153

"I suppose some will, Finn." Billy paused to hold up a specially fine lettuce. "What's brought this on?"

"Well, on St Agatha's team, they've got a girl. A girl! I mean, what will she know about conkers? They've no chance, have they?" Then he stopped and frowned.

"But Luke, who goes there, he said she's really good and she beats them all the time in the playground."

"Well then, you'll have to wait till you get to the contest. Girls can be pretty good sometimes."

"I'm not getting beaten by a girl. No way."

"You'll just have to be the best then, won't you? But, remember, that'll be her plan, too."

Finn stomped along the path beside his grandad, who was hiding a wry smile.

O N the morning of the fun day a whispered phone call brought a look of concern to Billy's face.

"That was your dad, Finn. It looks like the baby's on the way. He's going to ring again when there's more news."

"OK. But can we still go?"

Billy nodded.

"Of course we can. You go and get those conkers!"

Others might have enjoyed the pampered pets section or the old-fashioned carousels and cake walk, but Billy knew that for Finn the only important part of the afternoon was the conker competition.

They'd talked tactics on the way, Billy giving Finn the full benefit of his lifetime's experience, so he was a bit surprised to find that the small freckled girl from St Agatha's — sticking out her tongue the better to concentrate — was soon leading the field with her own well-strung monsters. They were like ball bearings in her hands.

When it came down to a final head to head between Finn and his ace opponent, Billy willed his grandson to use his superior strength to thrash his way to success. Sadly, a supreme smash from Freckleface sent Finn's conker flying from his hand.

Billy could see he was unnerved, recognising the way Finn's teeth dug into his bottom lip, and prayed silently for success.

A second later, Finn's conker was in bits, shattered by a killer blow. The lad shook hands with his opponent and walked away, head high and eyes stormy.

When Billy put Finn to bed that night he tried to lighten the mood.

"You did your best, Finn, that's all that matters!"

But Finn was still smarting from his defeat.

"She was a girl, Grandad. I was beaten by a girl!"

Heaton Moor Almshouses, Stockport

*I*N 1939, when I was eight, we moved from
  Manchester to live in the Stockport area, firstly in
Marple and then in Romiley.

My school was St Mary's in Marple Bridge, where a
Miss O'Doherty was the headmistress.

At the age of fourteen I began work in the Bee Hive,
Great Underbank.

On Sunday afternoons my mother and I would walk
along the side of the canal to Marple, then down
Brabyn's Brow for an ice-cream, and on to Marple
Bridge for the bus home to Romiley.

Such happy memories.

— *Mrs E.M.R-McC., Derby.*

J. CAMPBELL KERR.

"Well, never mind, son. Just remember, by this time tomorrow you'll be someone's big brother. Put conker competitions out of your mind and think on that instead!"

As Billy reached the door he heard Finn's voice once more.

"She was good, wasn't she, Grandad?"

✳   ✳   ✳   ✳

Grandma was already on the phone when Finn attacked his breakfast next morning. And she was smiling.

"Well?" Billy was asking. "Well?"

"The baby's here! Mother and baby doing well." She turned to Finn. "We'll just give your mum a couple of hours to get some sleep and then we'll have a drive to the hospital and see them both."

"OK." Finn didn't seem too bothered either way.

Maria and Billy were whispering between themselves over the washing-up, but Finn took no notice.

At the hospital, Finn's mother gave him a thorough kissing and told him how much she'd missed him.

"Have you been having a good time at your grandma's? Have you been a good boy?"

Finn assured her he had, on both counts.

"Would you like to see your little sister?"

"Sister?" Finn looked perplexed.

"Yes, love, you've got a gorgeous sister. Isn't she lucky, having a big brother like you to show her how to do everything and look after her?"

He sidled round to the far side of Mum's bed where the see-through crib held the new baby. He gazed at her for a while.

"What do you think?" Mum asked.

Finn shrugged.

"She's OK."

He looked up at Billy, who was watching him carefully.

"Grandad . . ." Finn's little finger was clasped in the grip of the baby's tiny hand. "Will she want to play conkers with me?"

"She might, Finn," Billy explained gravely. "When she gets a bit older, that is. Under your expert tuition she might become a world champion. Girls can be really good at things sometimes."

Finn was silent for a few seconds.

"S'pose," he said slowly. "But she'd better not beat me! Grandad?"

"What, Finn?"

"She's beautiful though, isn't she?" His eyes rested, love-struck, on his baby sister's face.

Billy smiled down at them.

"That she is, Finn. That she is." ▦

156

Illustration by Len Thurston.

"Dance With Me..."

by Deborah Tapper.

WHAT are you doing tonight, love?"

Ivy McKenzie turned round sharply, a snappy retort on her lips, and found herself studying the lean, smiling man lying in the narrow hospital bed. He was propped up on a pillow and his unbuttoned khaki jacket was draped around his shoulders for warmth.

Ivy noticed he was still wearing his uniform shirt underneath his jacket; the top three buttons were undone, exposing his throat and the smooth skin of his chest.

His bright brown eyes laughed up at her, and there was an irrepressibly merry grin on his face.

"Fancy a dance?" he went on in his chirpy Cockney accent. "We could clear the floor, ask the band to play something lively . . . . I'm pretty nimble on my pins, sweetheart."

157

Ivy caught herself smiling back at him and tightened her lips. A good many of the young volunteer nurses fraternised with the patients, but not her. She couldn't bring herself to be anything more than a caring presence to these young men who arrived at the field hospital every day to be treated, before either being sent home to dear old Blighty or straight back to the Front.

"I don't think you'll be dancing for a while yet, Mr . . ."

"Sid," he supplied. One bright brown eye closed in a wink.

He was hardly a man; to tell the truth, he wasn't much more than a boy. Ivy's quick gaze took in the cheerful face — brown eyes, straight nose, pale unshaven cheeks and that big optimistic smile — and guessed he was about eighteen, maybe nineteen at the most. Three years younger than herself.

"Sidney Francis Fisher." He grinned up at her. "That's me. Private Fisher of the First Battalion, London Regiment. So what's your name, darling?"

"I'm Nurse McKenzie."

"No — your first name."

He was looking at her so expectantly, she felt she had to answer.

"Ivy," she said reluctantly.

"Ivy . . . like in the song — the one where the ivy clings ever so tightly to the garden wall?"

When she nodded, another grin split his face. He winked again and whistled the opening few bars of the song.

"Tell you what, pretty Ivy — why don't you forget about the boring old wall and cling to me for a while instead?"

His brashness annoyed her all of a sudden and she put her nose in the air.

"I don't think so. Now if you'll excuse me, Private Fisher, I have other patients to attend to."

$$* \quad * \quad * \quad *$$

The war had changed everything.

Ivy thought about it as she lay in her bunk that night. She was exhausted, her feet aching from walking up and down the rows of injured men housed in the crowded field hospital, but sleep seemed as far away as her old life.

She turned on to her side, wondering how her two older brothers were faring. They had signed up early in 1915, eager to fight.

They had all gone to wave goodbye to Robert and Donald, and had stood on the platform until the last flags and streamers of white steam had faded away against the blue of a March sky, before the three of them — her mother, father and herself — had turned and walked slowly away.

Six months later, Ivy followed her brothers to France as a volunteer nurse.

Thinking about her brothers made Ivy remember the dances they had gone to in Edinburgh, when they stayed with Aunt Polly and Uncle Ernest for two months during the long, hot summer of 1913, just after her nineteenth birthday.

She smiled into the darkness, thinking how she had walked back between her tall, laughing brothers through the deepening twilight of a peaceful summer evening, their arms linked. Then she recalled all the young men who had politely asked her to dance.

If she liked them enough, she had let them walk her back to her aunt and uncle's house, and several of the young men had been bold enough to hold her hand as they strolled along behind her brothers.

But the war had changed all those young men just as surely as it was changing everything else. The wards were full of silly young boys like that Sid Fisher, who whistled and winked at her, or tried to talk her into kissing them while they did their best to slip their arms around her waist.

Her friend Elsie insisted that the lads only behaved this way because they were young and scared and a long way from home. Elsie was a lively lass from the Borders who enjoyed giggling and chattering with her patients and who knew how to hold her own if the light-hearted bantering took a more saucy turn — whereas Ivy tended to take everything rather seriously.

So seriously, in fact, that when she and Elsie had bickered over some trivial thing a few days earlier, her friend had called her prissy, and told her she was still as firmly trapped in the long-departed nineteenth century as a fly caught in a scrap of amber!

Ivy stared into the darkness, wondering if Elsie was right. She didn't think she was particularly old-fashioned or stuck-up. Her father was successful, admittedly — the last century had been very kind to Dr McKenzie — and his success meant they could afford several servants and the only motor vehicle in the neighbourhood.

She turned over on to her other side and found she was thinking about Sid Fisher again, with his mischievous grin and bright eyes. A cheeky wee tyke like that wouldn't have even dared talk to Dr McKenzie's only daughter before the war — yet there he was, lying wounded in bed, and he had the nerve to try to chat her up!

She wouldn't have spared him a second glance if she'd seen him at a dance! Ivy preferred men to be handsome and sophisticated; she wouldn't have looked twice at a chirpy Cockney lad like Sid Fisher.

So why couldn't she stop thinking about him? Ivy sighed. The world didn't make sense any more.

S HE noticed Sid was lying with his head turned patiently towards the doorway when she entered the ward the next day. He spotted her immediately and his face split into its impish grin, but she ignored him as she moved down the rows of beds in her blue nurse's uniform with its long white apron and the crisp white cap pinned to her glossy black hair.

When she finally reached his bed he was lying back on the pillow, looking even paler in the cold, greyish light of morning.

"So, Private Fisher," she said, stopping and looking down at him, her voice a careful balance between professionalism and compassion, "how are you this morning?"

THE brown eyes opened.
"Not so bad now you're here, pretty Ivy," Sid said, flashing her his sauciest smile.

"That's Nurse McKenzie to you, Private Fisher," Ivy said, but she found herself smiling back and even blushing a little as she plumped up his pillow.

"You're Scottish, aren't you?" Sid said. "I can tell by your accent."

"So you can — just like I can tell you're a London lad from yours."

"I went to Scotland once." A thoughtful look shaded his eyes as Sid settled back against his pillow.

Herbal Eyebright

AS its name may suggest, eyebright has a long folk medicine history of being used to treat eye ailments. In fact, it was even thought that eyebright could preserve eyesight and bring gladness into the life of the sufferer!

This elegant little plant with its pretty white and purplish flowers dates back to the time of the Ancient Greeks and was also traditionally used to treat allergies, hay fever, congestion and sinusitis.

"Did you now? And what did a London lad like you make of it?"

"I loved it," Sid said unexpectedly. "It was so beautiful, so wild . . . I'd never have believed there could be so much open space anywhere — or so much sky — if I hadn't seen it with my own eyes."

"A bit different from London, then?"

"Very different. I live in a tiny two-up, two-down terraced house in a long street that's so narrow the tradesmen can hardly get their carts down it. There are eight of us — Mum and Dad and the six of us kids — all squashed into those few rooms." The smile widened. "It's a bit of a squeeze, sometimes."

"I can imagine," Ivy said, but she couldn't.

"Where do you live?" Sid asked. "Are you a city girl, or do you live in some little village in the middle of nowhere?"

Ivy said nothing. She was thinking about the big stone house overlooking the loch.

"Maybe when this is all over I could see you again." Sid was gazing up at her, the brown eyes puppy-dog hopeful. "Maybe we could have that dance . . . ?"

Ivy looked at his eager face and decided to let him down gently.

"There's someone waiting for me, Sid," she said softly, not realising she had called him by his first name. "I'm sorry."

Young Private Fisher sighed and nodded. He even managed a rueful smile.

"I thought there might be," he said. "I just hope he realises how lucky he is."

*   *   *   *

"You said what? That was really mean of you!" Elsie put her hands on her hips and shook her head reproachfully at Ivy, tut-tutting like a disapproving
160

Know-how!

Although modern science has confirmed that eyebright is effective in treating pinkeye and other eye problems, it is not advised that anyone tries to make up a solution of this themselves as it may not be sterile and may cause more problems than it cures!

old lady. "Poor Sid Fisher! You know he likes you."

"Which is exactly why I said it." Ivy's cheeks flamed with sudden heat. "He likes me — and I don't like him."

"Are you sure about that?"

"Of course I am! I do know my own mind!" Ivy looked away, wishing her face didn't feel so hot. "He's nothing but a silly wee boy."

"He'll be twenty-one next month," Elsie said. "He told me."

"Well, he doesn't look it."

"You could have promised him a dance, at least! He's being moved tomorrow."

"Moved?" Ivy stopped in her tracks. "Where to?"

"He's going home," Elsie said. "He needs better treatment than we can give him here."

"And after he's convalesced — what then?" Ivy murmured, half to herself. "Back to the trenches . . . ?"

"All the more reason to have promised him that dance," Elsie said.

IN the end, Ivy did promise Sid Fisher a dance. She helped him into the waiting ambulance, then pressed his hands briefly, told him where she lived and promised she would dance with him once the war was over.

"Can I have something of yours, pretty Ivy?" Sid asked suddenly. "Just a little keepsake of some kind; something to remember you by."

"A keepsake?" she repeated.

"It would mean a lot to me."

Ivy was about to refuse him when Elsie's words flashed through her mind, and before she knew what she was doing, she had pulled a handkerchief from her pocket and given it to him.

Sid's fingers closed around the scrap of white linen, clutching it tightly, and he beamed at her. He was still beaming as the ambulance doors closed and the vehicle rumbled away.

Ivy stared after it, already regretting her impulsive action. Normally, she wouldn't have dreamed of making such a ridiculous romantic gesture. And it wasn't just any handkerchief; she had embroidered it herself, her name picked out in one corner with delicate tendrils of green ivy leaves curling around it. It was too personal a thing to have given to an impressionable young man like Sid Fisher.

Ivy sighed, watching the ambulance until it had rattled over the brow of the hill and was lost from sight.

She sighed again, then went inside, back to her other patients.

THE years went on. 1916 became 1917, then 1918. Ivy was kept so busy she almost forgot about Sid Fisher. Almost. But some nights, just as she was drifting into an exhausted sleep, the memory of his cheeky grin and twinkling brown eyes flashed into her mind.

After the Armistice, Ivy went home, arriving in time for a quiet Christmas in the big house on the hill above Inver. Her brothers followed her a month or so later. They were both different. Donald returned with a limp and a neat military moustache and an extensive vocabulary of cryptic Army slang, while cheerful Robert had become quiet and subdued, happy to sit in his favourite armchair all day with his ankles crossed and his chin propped in his hand, gazing out of the big picture window at the restless grey loch.

Of the three McKenzie siblings, Ivy considered herself to be the least changed, in spite of all that she had seen.

But the war had altered her world for good. Her father looked so much older and her mother had become nervous and over-protective.

Even the house seemed different. Ivy took to wandering through the rooms, touching the familiar furnishings, trying to convince herself that nothing had really altered, that just the right word or even the right glance could turn everything back to how it had been before she went away.

Deep down, though, she knew she didn't really want to turn everything back. She was the one that needed to change. She was still trapped, stuck fast in her block of amber, waiting for someone to come and free her.

      ✳   ✳   ✳   ✳

"There's a young fellow at the door, Miss Ivy."

Ivy looked up from her book. She was curled up in one of the big armchairs in front of the fire. The curtains were drawn against the winter night and a thin sleety rain rattled against the glass.

"At this time of night?" she exclaimed. "Who is it? Someone for my father?"

"He's asking to see you, miss." Old Mrs McRae looked disapproving. "He didn't tell me his name."

"Is it one of the local lads?"

The elderly housekeeper shook her head.

"I could barely understand a word he was saying, Miss Ivy, what with that accent of his. Shall I tell him you're not at home?"

"No." Slowly, Ivy put her book down and rose to her feet, her heart beginning to thump wildly.

Sid Fisher stood there, soaked to the skin, water streaming down his long grey coat and dripping off the brim of his hat. A battered case stood by his muddy shoes. He took the hat off, seeming oblivious to the rain and the

162

darkness, and gave her a cautious smile.

"Hello, Ivy," he said shyly.

For a few moments, Ivy just stood and stared at him, clinging to the doorjamb for support, her heart pounding. He had changed, along with everything else. The man standing on the doorstep with his dripping hat clasped in his hands and his lean, serious face was an older, more grown-up version of the cheery lad she remembered.

"Sid!" she gasped. "I never thought I'd see you again . . . !"

Then he grinned.

The cheeky grin transformed his face and his bright brown eyes twinkled. The rain was streaming off his dark hair and running down his cheeks, and Ivy suddenly realised how tall he was, and how handsome.

Next second, he dropped his hat (it landed in a puddle, but he didn't seem to notice or care), reached out to her — and then Ivy was wrapped in strong arms, both of them unmindful of the chilly rain as their lips met.

HOW did you find me?" she asked when they finally broke the kiss. "I would have come sooner but my mother was ill," Sid said. He was still holding her tightly, as if afraid to let her go. "As soon as she was well again, I caught the first train I could up to Edinburgh.

"You told me you lived near a little place called Inver, but when I got out at the station this morning, I found none of the trains went anywhere near it. One of the guards pointed me in the right direction and I managed to hitch a couple of rides on farm carts, but mostly I walked.

"When I got to Inver, I just knocked on every door I came to, asking if anyone knew Ivy McKenzie. Eventually, someone told me you lived in the house on the hill — and here I am."

"But you're wet through! Where are you staying?"

"Staying?" Sid blinked. "I don't know — I didn't think."

"Oh, Sid!" Ivy kissed him again. "You silly thing! You mean to say you walked all the way from Edinburgh, just to see me?"

Sid gazed at her, his brown eyes sparkling.

"I would have walked all the way from France. I kept thinking about you, about what it would feel like to see you again, to hold you in my arms and kiss you." He blushed a little as he spoke. "I've still got your handkerchief. I kept it folded up against my heart . . . so I could give it back to you one day."

There was a lump in Ivy's throat and her eyes prickled. She pressed her face against Sid's wet coat and held him close, wondering why she had ever let him go in the first place.

"So will you dance with me, pretty Ivy?" he said.

She answered him with another kiss, then rescued his hat from the puddle, took his hands and pulled him inside, into the warmth of the house.

"Of course I will," she said. "As many dances as you want." ■

That Day In December

"JOE, I'm falling!" I shouted desperately.

Joe stood at the foot of the tree and didn't even bother to look up at me. He was busy trying to disentangle a number of his mum's tea towels.

"No, you're fine," he answered, unconcerned.

"I'm falling, I tell you!" I insisted in my best drama-lesson voice.

"You won't fall," Joe said. "I know you."

That was the trouble. Joe did know almost everything about me. I say almost, because there was just one thing that he either didn't know or else did know but was politely ignoring.

It was true that I was steady on the branch. I was in no danger of slipping. Mum said I climbed trees like a monkey. Like a cat, Joe said.

In fact, one day Joe had even said, "Not bad for a girl — or a boy, come to think of it." That was high praise.

But physical steadiness aside, I was still falling. I was falling in love.

It was as if on my ninth birthday I had suddenly stopped seeing Joe as my current best friend. He was now transformed into my potential future boyfriend. These feelings changed my whole view of the world. The last two years no longer made sense just as a budding friendship — they were elevated to the status of early courtship. In a decade or so, we would be able to get married and hear people describe us as "childhood sweethearts".

I could picture it so clearly. We'd have a summer wedding. First there would be a ceremony at the little grey stone church in the village. Then there would be a big reception at a country hotel. I might even climb a tree in my wedding dress for old times' sake. It wouldn't matter if it got ripped or stained. It would be so romantic.

"BUDGE over," Joe said, clambering up beside me. He was ten and growing fast for his age, so he needed more branch-space than I did.

"Can you sort these out?" he asked, handing me the tangled tea towels which his mum had earlier fashioned into a headdress.

So here we were, in the mid-afternoon of a cold December day, Joe in his battered Joseph costume for the nativity play, and me in a long white dress with gold tinsel stapled to the hem.

I'd wanted to be Mary, of course, even before I knew that Joe would be cast as Joseph. But I had been made an angel, which wasn't fair as most of the best angels have male names like Gabriel — that's who I ended up as.

164

I suppose it was quite enjoyable, especially leading all the other girls and boys (who only had silver tinsel) down the aisle, singing "Hark! The Herald Angels Sing".

The nativity play had been held in the little church I'd already chosen for my far-distant wedding. We performed the play this morning, the day the school broke up for Christmas. Afterwards, there had been lots of exchanging of presents and smiles. Then we'd all gone home, still in our costumes. I'd sat next to Joe on the bus, whilst our mums chatted behind us.

Joe hadn't been very talkative. In fact, he'd seemed unusually thoughtful, turning his headdress over and over in his hands.

"Are your knuckles still sore?" I asked him, noticing that they hadn't yet healed. He'd fallen off his skateboard last week.

"You think you notice everything," he said strangely. "But you don't."

"What do you mean?"

He gave me the shrug he usually reserved for his mum when she asked him how his T-shirt had been torn or where he'd lost his shoe.

"Nothing, I suppose," he mumbled.

"My elbow's still bad," I said, trying to gain his approval. I twisted my arm so that he could see my very impressive war wound. Well, cycling injury, actually. My skirt had got caught in the chain.

"Why do you wear a skirt?" Joe had asked scathingly.

"Because I'm a girl," I'd answered crossly, "and it's about time you noticed that."

"But I've always noticed that."

Illustration by Gerard Fay.

He'd looked puzzled. "I know you're a girl. I'm just saying that if you're going to act like a tomboy then you should wear jeans."

He had a point. But jeans weren't romantic. Princesses and angels did not wear trainers and tracksuit bottoms. They had long hair and wore dresses.

by Lily Garth.

Sitting in the tree in our costumes, we disentangled the tea towels. Joe was still being uncharacteristically quiet. A little part of me hoped that maybe he had fallen in love with me, too, and that he didn't know how to tell me. But a bigger part of me knew that probably wasn't true.

Christmas was a hard time of year for us, as we'd both lost our dads in December. Mine had died five years ago on the twenty-second; Joe had lost his three years ago, on the twenty-eighth.

Sometimes I thought Joe was the only other person in the world who could understand how I felt about losing Dad. We didn't talk about it much, but it was a bond between us. I like to think that we comforted each other just by being there. It was part of our friendship.

"It's getting dark," I said. "Mum will want me indoors soon. Yours, too, I expect."

We were less than a hundred yards away from the flats where we lived, but three o'clock on a winter afternoon is a very different scenario from three o'clock in summer. It's also much, much colder and people should wear more than just a white dress with tinsel. Tinsel is not famous for its thermal properties.

Just then, Joe moved closer to me as if he was feeling the cold, too. He put his hand on my arm.

"We're moving," he said.

For a moment I thought he meant we as in him and me. For another moment I hoped that his "moving" was a variation of my "falling". Perhaps, whilst I was trying to say, "I'm falling in love with you", he was trying to say, "We're moving towards a future of wedded bliss".

Except, of course, Joe was a ten-year-old boy and they didn't say things like that, and as I was only a nine-year-old girl, I shouldn't have been dreaming of things like that anyway.

"Mum and I are going to live with my gran in the New Year," he said, still holding my arm. I felt his fingers tighten.

And after that, neither of us could speak. I couldn't even think. It hurt too much. After a while of sitting there in silence, we slowly climbed down and went indoors to our separate flats.

THE tree has gone. In fact, all the trees Joe and I used to climb have gone. More flats were built when I was a teenager, almost right down to the river's edge. It makes me feel sad. It also makes me feel cross with myself for not ever finding out what type of tree it was that played such an important role in my early friendship with Joe.

"Maybe Joe would remember," Mum says.

"Maybe," I say wistfully.

Mum gives me a light kiss on the cheek and then leaves me alone for a while with my memories. Perhaps I shouldn't have come back here today, but it seemed important.

After all, this was the place where I fell in love for the first time. What

166

better place to visit on my wedding day?

That last Christmas Joe and I spent here as children, before he went to live with his grandmother, we exchanged extra, goodbye gifts. I gave him a chisel which had belonged to my dad.

"Because you're practical," I explained in a strained voice, trying not to cry, "and you were Joseph, the carpenter, in the play." I took a deep breath. "And because if he'd ever had the chance to meet you, I think my dad would have really liked you."

Joe said thank you. Then he bit his lip. Finally, he held out my goodbye present.

"I've got to go now," he said, thrusting the small box at me. Then he turned and practically ran away from me.

Opening the box, I found myself staring at a block of white cheese. Quickly, I closed it again, and ran after Joe. When I caught up with him, he was on the point of getting into his grandma's car.

"What's this?" I asked.

"It's Cheshire cheese." He was very red in the face.

"But why?" I was puzzled.

"Because you're like the Cheshire cat." He looked at the ground. "You know, in 'Alice In Wonderland'. The Cheshire cat that sits in the tree, disappearing bit by bit until only the smile's left."

And then something amazing happened. Joe lifted his head and gazed directly into my eyes.

"You smile a lot," he said. "I like it. I'll remember that smile."

And, as it turned out, he did.

✳   ✳   ✳   ✳

"Darling!" Joe calls to me now.

I turn to greet him, giving him a huge kiss and holding him close. Then I beam up at him.

"See this smile?" I ask. "Well, you're responsible for it. You put it on my face."

Joe and I were married this morning. It was a summer wedding in the little grey stone church in the village. Now we're on our way to the country hotel for the reception, but we just wanted to stop here for a moment on our journey.

It's all so different from that cold, sad winter afternoon after the nativity play, when I was nine and Joe was ten. And yet, that day was part of our history, part of our story. Looking back, I wouldn't be without it.

My wedding dress is long and white with a little gold embroidery at the hem as a tribute to my angel costume's tinsel. This dress is far too glamorous to climb a tree in, and yet, I think I might be tempted to try if our tree was still here.

"I really landed on my feet when I fell in love with you," I tell Joe.

"But of course you did," he says, smiling. "Just like a cat." ▨

WHEN I was a little girl, I always said I'd never marry a farmer. Not for me the quiet countryside or remote hills. I wanted to live in a town with a dress shop, and a cinema, and exciting things to do. I wanted my husband to have a job with regular hours and clean shoes.

Funny how you end up doing the exact opposite from what you plan, isn't it? It never snows at Christmas any more. When I was little it snowed every year without fail, at least a sprinkle if nothing else — and those frosts! Where we lived, it was a winter wonderland.

I remember Dad telling me, one bright Christmas morning, how he and Uncle Dai used to use a tray for a sled.

"We didn't have money for fancy sleds. I can remember Granny Jenkins shrieking in horror when she saw me and Uncle Dai sitting on her best tin tray sliding down the hillside after Christmas lunch! You know, the one with the roses on it that Mum has now.

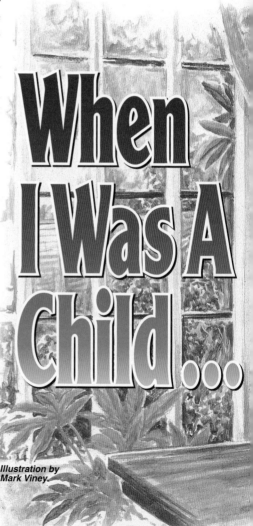

"There we were marauding down the hillside, and in our Sunday bests, too! I don't think we sat down for a whole week after she caught us."

"Oh, Da, Granny Jenkins was lovely. She would never have smacked you."

"Smacked us? No, love, she didn't. We got friction burns on our backsides from skidding over the hard snow; very sore, I can tell you!"

I miss those stories of Dad's. My boys would have had such a wonderful grandad.

The landscape I'm looking out on is so very different from the one I grew up with in Wales.

It'll be Christmas in a few weeks, yet the sky is as wide and clear and blue as a Welsh spring morning.

I want to make this Christmas special, though, because Mum's coming, and she deserves it.

She's had a tough few years

When I Was A Child...

Illustration by Mark Viney.

168

since we lost Dad. I want to give her happy new memories to go alongside the old ones.

Her grandsons will help make it special, too. She loves those boys with all her heart, and they her, even though they've not seen that much of her over the years.

I'm sure everything will be just fine. Just to be here with us all will be enough for Mum, and I can't wait to hug her.

Our huge tree is an artificial one, white, to remind us of the snow I love. It'll have twinkling fairy lights and all manner of decorations, just as the one at home used to.

We always had chocolate lanterns covered in bright foil paper, most of them eaten by Christmas Eve. Dad used to remodel the foil around a conker or something, so that Mum didn't know we'd already eaten them.

There are biscuits that I've baked specially, stars and moons and holly leaves, with silver berries, just like the ones I used to make with Mum.

I've made a Christmas cake. I mean to say, those shop cakes are all very nice, and a lot easier, I grant you.

But you can't beat the family recipe tried and tested over the years.

by Hilary Halliwell.

Mum will appreciate it, I just know she will.

I've got a kitchen with all mod cons, but Mum never had gadgets. Hers was a real farmhouse kitchen.

The lambs that were cast off always ended up in Mum's care. Sometimes at Christmas an early one would be at the bottom of the stove in a box, with Mum feeding it from a bottle what seemed like every five minutes.

I loved those lambs, their warm soft mouths sucking away at life, never giving up. I'm sure they thought Mum was their mother.

I can't believe that by tonight she'll actually be here, in our house, sampling my cake and looking at our tree! It's three years since we've seen her, and I can't imagine where all that time has gone.

But Mum understands, that comes out in every phone call.

"I DO miss you, Bronnie. I wish you were here so that I could help you out with those boys of yours. How are they, my fine big lads?"

"Why don't you come and see for yourself how they've grown? We'd love to see you, I'd love to see you! We could help out with the fare —" I'd tailed off, because I'd knew what the answer would be before she said it.

"I can't, Bronnie. I'm too set in my ways. Besides, you know what Dad always said about flying! If God had meant us to fly, he'd have given us wings. I'd be so nervous, all that way . . ."

Then, out of the blue, Uncle Dai had phoned me.

"She's coming, Bronnie! I told your mam, in no uncertain terms. 'Bronnie needs you. It's been far too long, Sylvie, and I'm paying!'

"It'll do her no end of good. She'll be with you for Christmas. I'll put her on the plane myself."

Well, that's Uncle Dai for you. I couldn't speak, I was so happy.

Now, at last, we pile into the station wagon and head for town. The local plane will land this afternoon and bring me Mum.

Andrew is a wonderful husband. He knows how much this all means to me. Though I never planned to marry a farmer, I'm glad I did. We met when he came to live on a hill-farm for a year.

He squeezes my hand as he drives. Looking across at him, I know what keeps me here, so far from Mum and my Welsh roots.

The small plane makes its usual bumpy, unceremonious landing. A bit like Dad and Uncle Dai on the tray all those years ago, only it doesn't land in soft white snow but red dust clouds which billow up, obscuring my view as the handful of passengers alight.

Then the dust clears, and my eyes fill up.

"Mum!" I run towards her. I would know her among a thousand people even with the lights out! She hasn't changed a bit. Maybe a few more silver hairs, but her clear blue eyes are the same as they've always been, even after a journey of two days.

Willie Shand.

Winter Morning

FROST paints the world with
 sparkling white,
There's a soft and hazy shifting light,
Strange winter beauty, cold and still,
Pale mist drifting, ghostly, chill.

Winter roses all tremble today,
Ice-cold petals folded, pray;
Water beads, like precious pearls,
Coolly glint on velvet furls.

Now the autumn leaves are lost,
Twisted branches shine with frost;
Sunlit ice may melt away,
But, in the shadows, frost will stay.

And, though the winter arms enfold,
I've seen a glimpse of morning gold,
A mellow gleam through ashen air,
A gift, a hope, a pledge, a prayer.
— ***Enid Pearson.***

We stand there wrapped in one another's arms, our tears of joy mingling. I'm the happiest woman alive.

The boys have caught up with us.

"Nanny, you're here! Look, Dad, Nanny's here!"

"Look at my two fine boys. Goodness, how tall you are — how handsome, just like your da."

They giggle and hang on to her waist just like I used to all those years ago, and my heart glows.

Mum's eyes widen with excitement as we drive home, taking in all the sights and sounds, new to her as they were to me, over fifteen years ago now.

I look at her hand clasped in mine, with the lines of life etched over it — a life full of hard work, yet tremendous happiness.

"Oh, Mum, I'm so glad you came!"

"It's all so big, love!" she says. "What would your dad have made of all this? I wish he could have seen it with me, Bronnie. I wish he could have seen the boys . . ." Her voice trails off.

Now I see new tears glisten in her clear blue eyes and press her hand.

EARLY the next morning I'm up and about. For the first time this year, I feel Christmas is well and truly in the air. I titivate the tree, and prepare food for Christmas Eve — tomorrow. I make yet more mince-pies, and Mum's favourite welsh cakes, though I doubt they'll be as good as hers.

Mum must be absolutely worn out, I think as I wrap more gifts for her. The boys are sworn to silence as they sit and watch Christmas TV beside the white sparkling tree.

I'm sure one or two of those chocolate lanterns have changed shape since the last time I looked. But who cares?

"Will Nanny get up soon? I want to show her all my things!" That's Matthew.

"Me, too. I love Nanny!" Jason can't be left out.

"Nanny's come a long way, and she's not used to aeroplanes. You leave her to rest."

"Don't you be too sure, my girl! Us hill-farmers are made of stern stuff!"

Mum is standing there, gifts in her arms, smiling. I want to jump into her arms and be little Bronnie again.

She sets her gifts with the rest around the tree, returns to her room, and reappears, holding what looks to be a very heavy gift indeed.

"Bronnie, I want you to have this." It's difficult for her to hold. As she gingerly hands it to me, it weighs a ton.

"Mam, how on earth did they let you take this on the plane?" I put it on the kitchen table with a thump.

"I had to cut down on what I brought, I can tell you, but I wanted you to have it, Bronnie. I hope you like it . . ."

We sit at the table and I peel away the paper. I can't believe what I see there before me.

"Remember what it is, then, do you?"

"Grandma's griddle-stone, for the welsh cakes! Oh, Mam!"

She darts off again and returns with something else.

"And this is for all of you."

I unwrap an old biscuit tin, and open it. Oh, that smell! Mum's welsh cakes.

"Mam, you've brought me Wales for Christmas. Yourself, and Grandma's griddle, and you made us welsh cakes . . ."

"Bake-stones, we always called them when I was a girl!"

I don't let on that I've already made some. Mine will taste nothing like hers!

AND so our Christmas begins in earnest — a warm and dusty, very different sort of Christmas. But it's none the worse for that. "That Christmas cake is wonderful, Bronnie. Grandma would be proud of you!" Mum says when she tastes it.

And on Christmas morning an orphan lamb sleeps soundly in a box in my hi-tech kitchen. Mum says it took a lot of feed at breakfast.

"You've the gift, Mam," Andrew says gently. "She'll do well with you looking after her."

We listen to endless memories about Grandma, how she used to pay sixpence to Mr Pugh, the baker, to have the Christmas cake baked in his oven. The boys love every single story.

And on Christmas Day there are two more surprises. The tea tray with the roses on it belong to my boys now. Mum's brought it halfway across the world.

And come the autumn, in March, Mum will be back again.

Our roots will always be in Wales, and some wonderful memories, too, but I married an Australian farmer, and our station has all the excitement I'll ever need.

And soon Mum will be here all the time to share it with me. My happiness is complete, except for a sprinkling of snow. I must get some artificial snow next year . . . ■

Printed and Published in Great Britain by D.C. Thomson & Co., Ltd., Dundee, Glasgow and London.

ISBN 978 1 84535 324 7
EAN 9 781845 353247

Lerwick, Shetland Isles